Common African Mosquitos
and their Medical Importance

J. D. GILLETT, O.B.E., D.Sc.

(Professor of Biology and Head of the School of Biological Sciences at Brunel University, Uxbridge, England: formerly Assistant Director of the East African Virus Research Institute, Entebbe, Uganda)

With 48 Colour Illustrations by
JUDITH G. SMITH, B.Sc., Ph.D.

(Senior Research Assistant in the Department of Biology, Brunel University)

 WILLIAM HEINEMANN MEDICAL BOOKS LTD : *London*

First Published 1972

© J. D. GILLETT 1972

ISBN 0 433 11750 8

To Yovani Ssenkubuge

Printed in Great Britain by John Swain & Co. Ltd., London

CONTENTS

FOREWORD V

INTRODUCTION I
    Mosquitos and Closely Related Flies I
    Genera and Subgenera 2
    Species, Subspecies and Varieties 3
    The Illustrations 3
    How to Use This Book 4

IDENTIFICATION OF GENERA 5

DESCRIPTIONS OF SPECIES 7
    Anopheles 8
    Ficalbia 34
    Coquillettidia 36
    Mansonia 48
    Hodgesia 52
    Aedeomyia 54
    Eretmapodites 56
    Aedes (Finlaya) 62
    Aedes (Stegomyia) 68
    Aedes (Aedimorphus) 84
    Aedes (Neomelaniconion) 90
    Aedes (Diceromyia) 92
    Culex 94

REFERENCES 104

INDEX TO VIRUSES 104

INDEX TO SPECIES 105

FOREWORD

During the many years that I spent in tropical Africa I was continually being made aware of the need for a book that would help the non-specialist to identify common mosquitos. The standard textbooks on African mosquitos are really too comprehensive and detailed for the non-specialist to use easily (Evans, 1938; Edwards, 1941; Hopkins, 1951; Gillies and de Meillon, 1968). I had in mind a different kind of book altogether, a book designed to help the people in the rapidly developing countries of Africa to identify their own mosquitos and to see at a glance which are of medical importance; a book that not only confined itself to the species of mosquitos most likely to be encountered, but limited its technical jargon to the minimum compatible with clarity and reliability.

This is the aim I have set myself in preparing the present book. In no way is it intended to replace or rival the standard texts, but rather to complement them and then only in a limited sense; it is a handbook to be used by medical officers, health workers, research staff, technicians and field workers, people who may be specialists in other fields but without detailed knowledge of the comparative anatomy and taxonomy of mosquitos. It can, in fact, be used by anyone who finds himself dealing with mosquitos in one way or another, or who wishes merely to identify those species that come his way.

It is many years now since I first thought of producing this book, the plan being to follow each page of descriptive text with a clear picture, in colour, showing as much detail as one might reasonably expect to see under a powerful handlens or under a low-power dissecting microscope. When I left Africa in 1962 I had already accumulated a small collection of some 60 species of mosquitos for this purpose; I brought this back with me, planning to photograph each species. It soon became apparent, however, that photographs did not show clearly enough the various points made in the text and it was going to be necessary to have paintings made of each species. Two major problems had to be overcome: first to find an artist who could not only tackle this sort of detailed work accurately, but would be able to give full time to the job; second to find the money to pay for the paintings and for making and printing high quality plates from them—a very expensive undertaking.

I was extremely fortunate in obtaining the services of Dr. Judith Smith who as artist and entomologist, combined the right qualities to undertake this task. The results exceed my best hopes and will, I think, go a long way in persuading people to take up the study of these often beautiful insects which are of such importance to mankind. Dr. Smith also undertook the line-drawings that occur in the text and has been most helpful in suggesting ways round some of the many problems that have occurred.

The cost of the paintings and for their reproduction in the book has been covered by a handsome grant from The Wellcome Trust. I am indebted to the Trustees for this generous help and to Dr. P. O. Williams and Dr. B. E. C. Hopwood in particular for the interest and enthusiasm they have shown for this project. The Trustees wisely insisted that the final selling price of the book be low enough to ensure its availability to the people for whom it is intended—that is the research worker and others dealing with mosquitos in the developing countries of Africa. This requirement has been met by the size of the grant. I am also indebted to Dr. J. Topping, Vice-Chancellor of Brunel University for extending Dr. Smith's Senior Research Assistantship beyond the period allowed for in the original grant.

Because of the high cost involved, it was necessary to limit the number of species to be described and painted to 48 and a difficult decision had to be made on which species to include and which to exclude. The selection was partly decided by availability, but careful consideration was paid to the general distribution of each species in the continent and to its importance both to medicine and as a pest. A few species have also been included which, although of no special importance, are commonly encountered either as resting adults or from collections of larvae. Anyone involved in the identification of mosquitos will find that it is sometimes necessary to reassure his fellow men that a particular species, although common, is in fact harmless. Also, anyone becoming interested enough to rear mosquitos through from larval collections may sooner or later wish to identify some of the more striking adults emerging from these.

My own collection came almost entirely from the Entebbe area. Fortunately Uganda, although politically part of East Africa, forms the meeting point of western and eastern faunas and floras. Indeed, in some ways, it is more typical of West Africa than of East. I discussed the book with Mrs. Ellinor van Someren when I visited Nairobi in 1969, and I am indebted to her for enabling me to make up some serious gaps in the East African species by allowing me to use some specimens from her own very fine collection. I am also extremely grateful to her for checking the accuracy and general workability of the descriptions. I must, however, take full responsibility for any mistakes and short-comings that may be found and I shall be grateful for comments and criticisms by those who come to use the book.

Dead specimens, however well preserved, do not always give accurate information on shape and colour; the abdomen can flatten or shrival, eyes usually change colour. It was necessary, therefore, to supplement some of the preserved material by living and freshly killed specimens. These were provided by Mr. Angus McCrae and I am most grateful to him and to the Director of the East African Virus Research Institute, Dr. W. G. Kafuko, for their co-operation; the care taken by Mr. McCrae to ensure rapid delivery of the specimens in London was much appreciated and admired.

I am greatly indebted to Mrs. Carol James, who patiently typed and re-typed the rather exacting MS a number of times. Finally I would like to record the pleasure it has been working with Mr. Dennis Holt of John Swain and Son Ltd. and Mr. Owen R. Evans, Managing Director of William Heinemann Medical Books Ltd. Mr. Holt has given expert advice and taken great pains in reproducing the colour illustrations from the original paintings and has personally supervised the four-colour printing from these.

September 1971   J.D.G.

INTRODUCTION

Mosquitos and closely related flies

It is surprising how many times mosquitos, sent in for identification or to back up a complaint, turn out not to be mosquitos at all. The commonest non-mosquitos that make up these collections belong to the family Chironomidae; these flies are closely related to mosquitos and resemble them in general appearance. Both the chironomids and the mosquitos (or culicids) belong to the Nematocera, one of several suborders of the Diptera or two-winged flies. Fortunately, there are a few points of difference which are immediately obvious and once these have been noted members of the two families can be separated without difficulty. These may be summarised thus:

Family Chironomidae (lake flies or non-biting midges)	Family Culicidae (mosquitos)
Usually rest with *front legs* raised.	Usually rest with *hind legs* raised.
Abdomen upturned at tip.	Abdomen not upturned at tip.
Mouthparts short (*no proboscis*).	Mouthparts long (proboscis).

Subfamilies and Tribes

The Culicidae or mosquitos are divided into three subfamilies: Anophelinae, Toxorhynchitinae and Culicinae, all three of which are represented in the African continent. The Culicinae make up most of them and are further divided into two tribes: the Sabethini and Culicini. Each subfamily and tribe is represented by one or more genera and these are divided into species; local forms of the species are known as subspecies. The scheme which follows sets out these details down to genera. The names following some of the generic names are those which may be encountered in older books; the number shown after each generic name indicates the number of African species in that genus (excluding Madagascar).

Order DIPTERA
    Suborder NEMATOCERA
        Family Culicidae
            Subfamily Anophelinae

Genus *Anopheles*	100

            Subfamily Toxorhynchitinae

Genus *Toxorhynchites* = *Megarhinus*	11

            Subfamily Culicinae
                Tribe Sabethini

Genus *Malaya* = *Harpagomyia*	8

                Tribe Culicini

Genera *Ficalbia*	16
Coquillettidia = *Taeniorhynchus* or *Mansonia*	19
Mansonia = *Taeniorhynchus*	2
Uranotaenia	31
Hodgesia	4
Orthopodomyia	1
Aedeomyia = *Aedomyia*	2
Eretmapodites	33
Aedes = *Aëdes*	157
Culiseta = *Theobaldia*	2
Culex	107

Genera and Subgenera

Some of the genera containing many species are divided for convenience into two or more subgenera. The names of subgenera are written in parentheses immediately following the generic name.

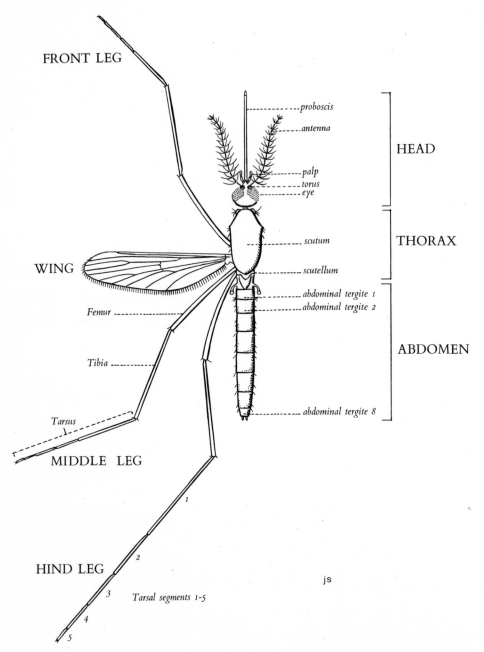

FIG. 1. Diagram of generalised mosquito showing the main characters used in identification.

By international agreement the name of the genus and that of the subgenus are written with a capital letter, while the name of the species always starts with a small letter, even when it is named after someone: for example *Aedes* (*Stegomyia*) *simpsoni*, where *Aedes* is the genus, (*Stegomyia*) the subgenus and *simpsoni* the species (named after Simpson). In this book only the genus *Aedes* has been divided into subgenera.

Species, Subspecies and Varieties

The question of what constitutes a species, as distinct from a subspecies or a variety is a difficult one, even for the specialist. Indeed, specialists do not always agree. The whole subject, fascinating and important though it is, is extremely complex and is really beyond the scope of this book. The reader who is interested should consult the specialist literature on the subject; the biological criteria for specific and subspecific rank, which have been generally accepted for the past thirty years, are clearly set out by Mayr (1942).

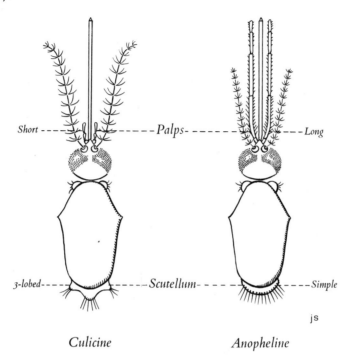

FIG. 2. Diagrams of the head and thorax, indicating the main points of distinction between female culicine and anopheline mosquitos.

Similarities in pattern and colour are, unfortunately, not always reliable guides to kinship. Nor do the lack of them necessarily indicate divergence. The cosmo-African *Anopheles coustani* has now been split into six different species on the grounds that some of the 'forms' occupy the same region and yet remain distinct. In my opinion, however, there is not yet enough evidence to support this step; they might equally well be regarded as members of a single polymorphic species. There is some evidence suggesting that certain forms of *A. coustani* feed on man more readily than others, but then so do certain populations of *Aedes aegypti* and *A. simpsoni*.

The Illustrations

The illustrations that accompany each description have been made after a detailed examination of several female specimens of each species. Wherever possible the most 'typical' specimen has then been selected as a model for the painting. Some of the illustrations are thus faithful copies made from single specimens. Most of them, however, have had to be based on several specimens.

All the illustrations are to the same scale (12 times the average size of the specimens). Actual specimens, however, will be found to vary in size very greatly; they may be considerably larger or very much smaller than the illustration indicates. For this reason no wing, body and leg measurements are given. Instead each species is allotted to one of the five following categories: very small, small,

3

medium, large, and very large. The well known *Aedes aegypti* ranges from very small to large—although most specimens of this species would be included in the small-to-medium range.

In each illustration the three pairs of legs are set out in a formal manner and the wings are shown drawn up at right angles to the abdomen. Special care must be taken when interpreting the patterns of spots, rings and stripes on the legs, since the front of the leg or the outside may be different from the opposite surface. In each illustration the surface that gives the most useful information has been depicted. Moreover, this is not always the same surface throughout the length of a single leg. For example, in *Mansonia africana* and *M. uniformis* the hind femur is shown in front view, while the tibia of the same leg is shown in hind view and the five tarsal segments in outer (or top) view. This procedure may at first seem confusing, but it should become perfectly clear when the book comes to be used. Indeed, it was found to present the easiest method of conveying the relevant information, provided that each illustration is used in combination with the simple description on the opposite page.

The characteristic purple and green sheen of the wings, which can be very confusing to the beginner, is here depicted on the right wing only. Whether this sheen is seen on the actual specimen to be identified will depend on the angle at which the wing is viewed.

How to Use This Book

The way in which this handbook is used will depend largely on the experience of the user. In general I would suggest the following procedure: first try to establish the genus of the specimen by reference to the important generic points set out below (having, of course, already familiarised oneself with the necessary technical terms shown in Figures 1 and 3). Then compare the specimen with the coloured plates included in that genus and, finally check the specimen against the description—point by point—referring to the illustration opposite for clarification whenever necessary. If the species in question is not included in the book then one will have to satisfy oneself with running it down to genus only.

No descriptions are included of any of the species belonging to the genera *Toxorhynchites*, *Malaya*, or *Uranotaenia* (none of which feeds on man) or of the genera *Orthopodomyia* and *Culiseta* (the few species of which are either very local or rarely found). If a specimen is considered to belong to one of these five genera it will, for example, have to be labelled merely as *Toxorhynchites* sp. or *Uranotaenia* sp. (sp. is used as an abbreviation for unidentified species). The same will apply even if the specimen does belong to one of the nine genera included in the book, but is not one of the species shown; the genera *Anopheles*, *Aedes* and *Culex* contain very many species which it has not been possible to include. Where closely related species cannot readily be distinguished, then all one can record is that the specimen belongs to a particular species-complex or group. For example, a specimen may have to be labelled as belonging to the *Anopheles funestus* complex or to the *Eretmapodites chrysogaster* group.

IDENTIFICATION OF GENERA

The arrangement of the genera in this book is based on the one given by Stone, Knight and Starcke (1959) in their catalogue of the mosquitos of the world. While there is no difficulty in separating the three genera *Anopheles*, *Toxorhynchites* and *Malaya*, some of the other genera are not so easy to recognise without a fairly detailed knowledge of mosquito anatomy. The following notes based on those given by Edwards (1941) should help (not all of these genera are shown in this book).

Anopheles: Wings speckled with dark and pale-coloured scales; female palps almost as long as the proboscis; scutellum single-lobed. When resting the abdomen is usually held up at an angle from the surface on which the mosquito is standing, forming a straight line with the proboscis. This genus includes the transmitters of human malaria.

Toxorhynchites: Very large, brightly coloured mosquitos with long proboscis, the last half of which curves sharply downwards. These mosquitos do not suck blood and are not included in the main section of this book (for a colour-plate of one of these strikingly beautiful mosquitos the reader is referred to the author's book, "Mosquitos"). The genus is important because the larvae feed on the aquatic stages of other mosquitos.

The culicines, which make up the remaining genera, all have the following characters in common; the female palps are much shorter than the proboscis; the scutellum is three lobed; when resting the abdomen is usually held parallel with the surface on which the mosquito is standing.

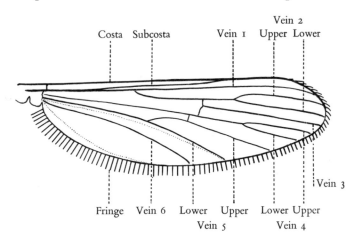

FIG. 3. Diagram of a mosquito's wing showing the names used in describing the veins; note that veins 2, 4 and 5 fork to give upper and lower branches.

Malaya: Very small culicines with a swollen tip to the modified proboscis, which is used to feed on juices supplied by ants. They do not suck blood and are not described further in this book.

Ficalbia: Small to large culicines without clearly defined characters. *Proboscis* somewhat swollen at tip (especially in the males); *legs* with conspicuous bristles on tibiae.

Coquillettidia: Except for *C. metallica*, most species are easy to recognise by their bright metallic yellow (or green) colour, and dark rings on legs. Larvae with breathing-siphon modified for piercing plant-tissues.

5

Mansonia: Medium-sized robust-looking culicines. *Wings* clothed with broad scales of mixed colours (brown and white); *legs* with conspicuous pale rings. Larvae with breathing-siphon modified for piercing plant-tissues.

Uranotaenia: Small culicines with short fork to wing-vein 2 and with vein 6 ending level with base of vein 5.1. *Wing-membrane* apparently lacking micro-hairs; wing-scales mostly broad; *abdomen* blunt-tipped; segment 1 scaly.

Hodgesia: Very small dark culicines with patch of silver-white scales on front of head. *Proboscis* not swollen at tip; *wing*—membrane with micro-hairs; outstanding wing-scales long, narrow and notched at tip; vein 6 ending level with base of 5.1.

Aedeomyia: Small to medium-sized culicines with short, broad wings clothed with broad scales of mixed colours. *Proboscis and legs* with pale rings.

Eretmapodites: Medium to large culicines with long slightly curving proboscis and long slender legs. *Eyes* widely separated by patch of silver-white scales; *abdomen* (narrow when viewed from above) dark with silvery patches above and golden scales below.

Aedes: Medium to large culicines *most* of which have pointed abdomen and well separated eyes.

(*Mucidus*): Very large robust and scaly *Aedes* with pointed abdomen and very long scaly legs.

(*Finlaya*): Medium-sized *Aedes* with silver-white or non-metallic pale markings on thorax and femora. *Abdomen* with segment 8 longer than broad.

(*Stegomyia*): Medium-sized *Aedes* usually with silver-white markings on a dark thorax and banded black and white hind tarsi.

(*Aedimorphus*): Medium to large *Aedes*. *Thorax* with or without distinctive ornamentation; *eyes* only narrowly separated. There are more than 50 species in this subgenus.

(*Neomelaniconion*): Medium-sized dark coloured *Aedes* with unbanded tarsi, and yellow or pale margins to thorax.

(*Diceromyia*): Small *Aedes* with basal pale rings on tarsal segments and broad wing-scales of mixed colours resembling those of *Mansonia*.

(*Skusea*): Represented in Africa by a single species, *Aedes pembaensis*, an almost entirely black *Aedes* without special markings except for white lateral triangles on abdomen. Head and scutellum covered with flat scales. Very common on the East African coastal region, feeding on man both inside and outsides houses. The larvae are found in crab holes.

Culiseta: Only two species in Africa both of which are large with blunt-tipped abdomen. *C. longiareolata* may be recognised by the leading edge of the costa, which is entirely pale-scaled, and by the dark spots at the base of veins 2, 3 and 5.1. Femora and tibiae speckled rather as in *Culex tigripes* (see page 95). *C. fraseri* is all dark except for a white ring at the base of the first tarsal segment on all legs.

Culex: Small to large culicines with blunt-tipped abdomen and usually (but not always) lacking distinctive markings. *Legs* with pad-like *pulvilli* between the claws.

DESCRIPTIONS OF SPECIES

The arrangement of species is based on those given in the four standard textbooks covering the African continent south of the Sahara: Evans (1938) and Gillies and de Meillon (1968) for the anophelines; Edwards (1941) and Hopkins (1951) for the culicines.

In the descriptions which follow, the various regions and parts of the body are included only when they are useful for identification by simple means. The main terms are used in the following way:

> *Head* refers to the top of the head only, that is the region behind the eyes, or, between and behind the eyes.
>
> *Thorax*, unless otherwise stated, refers to the upper or dorsal surface (or *scutum*) only.
>
> *Abdomen*, unless otherwise stated, refers to the upper or dorsal surface, consisting of the eight abdominal segments known as tergites 1-8.

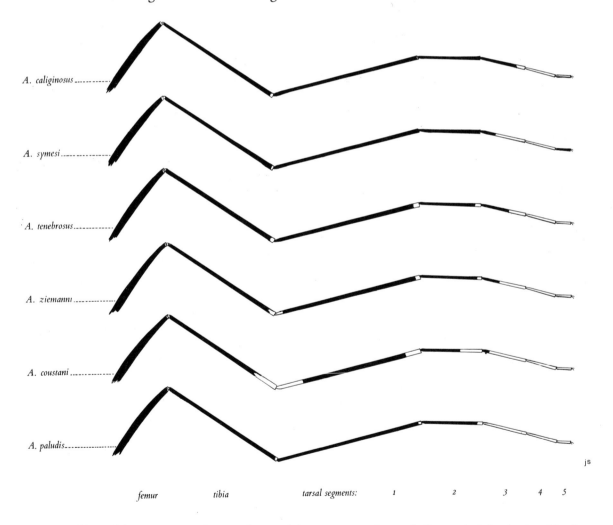

FIG. 4. Hind legs of the six species making up the *Anopheles coustani* complex; each diagram includes the tip of the femur and the whole of the tibia and tarsus.

Anopheles coustani complex

Large dark anophelines with shaggy palps and partly white hind tarsi; a complex of six closely related forms, now regarded as separate species, which may be arranged in a rough series grading from the very dark *A. caliginosus* through *A. symesi*, *A. tenebrosus*, *A. ziemanni* and *A. coustani* to the paler *A. paludis*.

Palps: Dark and very shaggy, usually with four pale rings including one at the tip; the first pale ring very small in some specimens; the pale rings reduced in size or even absent in *A. caliginosus*.

Thorax: Yellow hairs on a dark background; some white scales in middle at front end.

Wings: Conspicuously dark-scaled, usually with only two small white areas on costa (the first just beyond the middle, the second near the wing-tip); these white areas may be absent altogether (*A. caliginosus*) or more extensive (*A. paludis*).

Legs: Front and Middle }—dark but usually with pale rings at tips of most segments.

Hind —as shown in Fig. 4 on previous page.

Abdomen: Hairy with a tuft of dark scales on the underside of segment 7.

Distribution: *A. coustani* and *A. paludis* very widespread (even in highlands).
A. ziemanni very widespread especially in W. Africa.
A. symesi and *A. tenebrosus* East Africa and E. Congo.
A. caliginosus Katanga and Botswana.

Feeding Habits: Cattle and other animals, also man, mostly by night but by day in shady places (sometimes enters slowly moving vehicles).

Resting Habits: Rarely in houses; common in cattle-sheds.

Disease Transmission: Not important—possibly an occasional transmitter of malaria in local areas.

Breeding Places: Natural waters, with emergent or floating vegetation; the larvae are usually the most commonly found anophelines in any region.

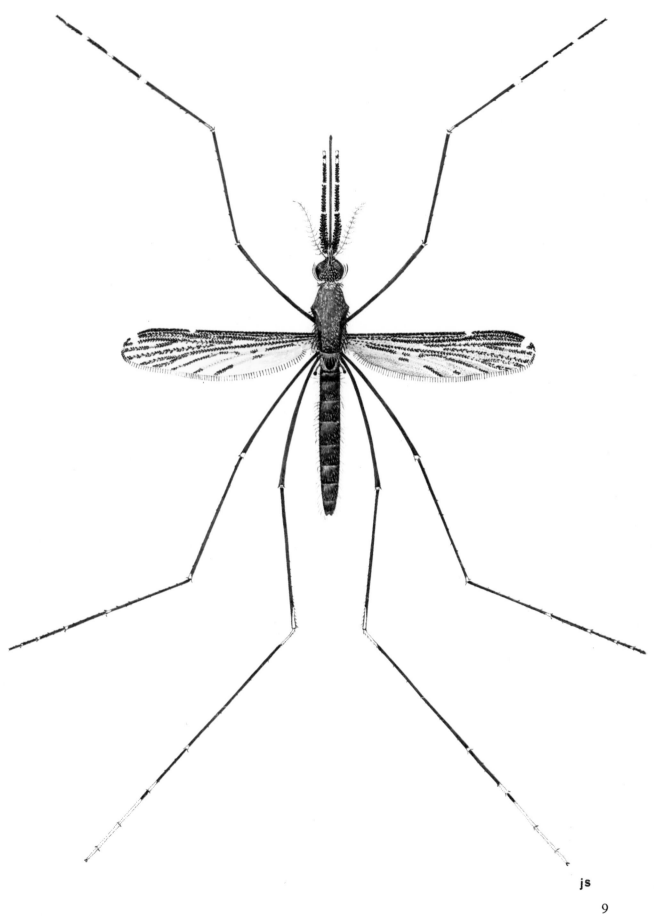

js

9

Anopheles implexus

Very large anopheline with conspicuous tufts on each side of the abdomen; partly white hind tarsi and speckled legs.

Palps: Shaggy and uneven in width with four pale rings including one at the tip.

Thorax: Yellowish hairs and scales on a velvety-brown background.

Wings: Pale scales more yellow than white, and variable in extent.

Legs: Front and Middle } — Femora and tibiae speckled or banded.

              Tarsi — segments 1–4 with pale ring at base; segment 5 — all dark.

        Hind   — Femur and tibia speckled or banded.

              Tarsus — segment 1 — pale ring at tip; narrow row of pale scales underneath;

                  segments 3 & 4 — entirely pale or with narrow dark bands at base;

                  segment 5 — dark with pale tip (all dark in some specimens).

Abdomen: Large lateral tufts of scales on either side of segments 1–7; each of these segments also has two silver-white spots on the underside.

Distribution: A common forest mosquito found over a wide area of Africa.

Feeding Habits: Mainly on cattle but includes man, particularly in certain regions. Feeds mainly by day in some areas, by night in others.

Resting Habits: On trunks of trees.

Disease Transmission: Not important.

Breeding Places: In forest pools, often associated with wild palms.

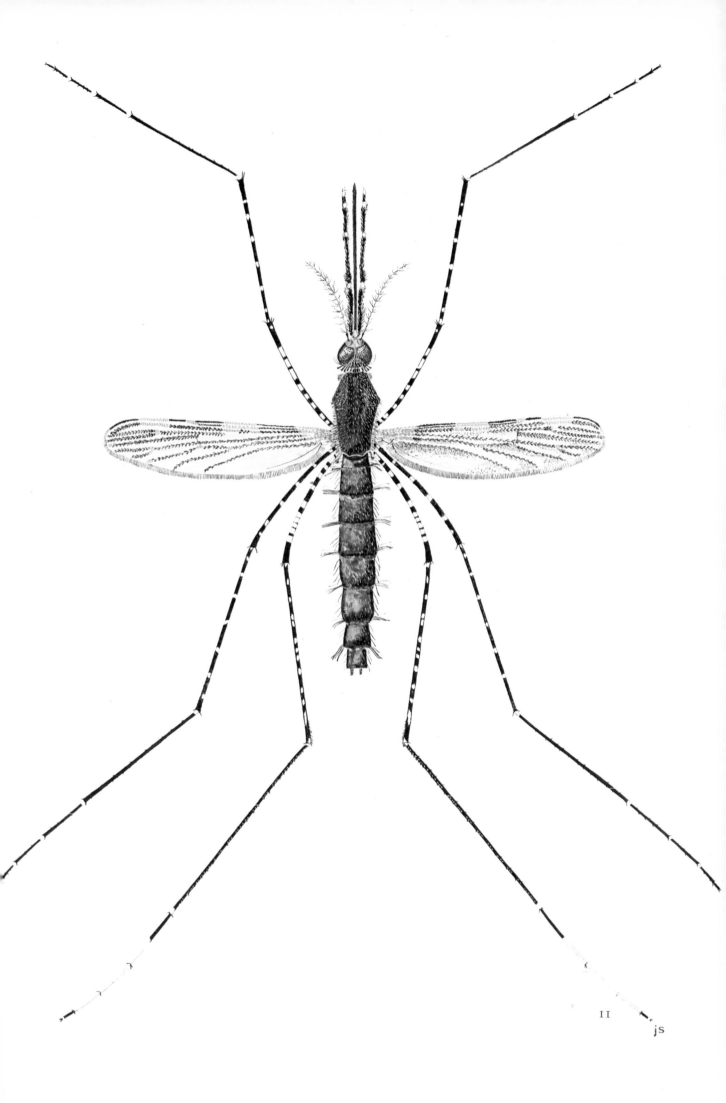

II   js

Anopheles nili group

Small anophelines with dark palps except for single pale ring at tip; the group includes *A. somalicus* as well as dark- and pale-winged *A. nili*.

Palps: Smooth and dark except for pale tip.

Thorax: Tuft of white scales at front end, otherwise scaleless.

Wings: Mainly dark-scaled with pale interruptions of costa few and short (pale areas more extensive in some Congo specimens).

Legs: Dark except for pale spots at tips of tibiae, and occasionally at tips of femora as well.

Abdomen: No scales.

Distribution: Very widespread throughout the continent south of the Sahara (*A. somalicus* can be separated only in the larval stage from typical dark *A. nili*).

Feeding Habits: Man and other mammals, mostly at night.

Resting Habits: Inside houses in certain areas; mainly outside in others.

Disease Transmission: Important transmitter of human malaria in certain regions.

Breeding Places: Commonly found among floating and emergent plants along the edges of streams and rivers.

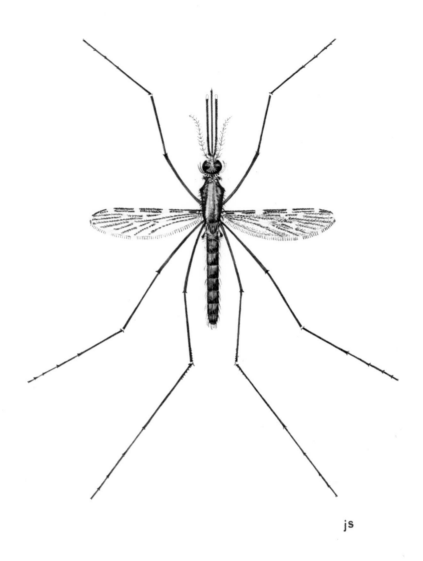

js

13

Anopheles rhodesiensis

Medium-sized anopheline with wing-scales all dark except along the leading edge.

Palps:	Dark and smooth with three very small pale rings including one at tip.
Thorax:	Scattered short hairs on a shiny background.
Wings:	Wing-scales without pale patches, except for four main pale interruptions along the costa and vein 1, the fourth at tip of wing (*A. rhodesiensis rhodesiensis*); these are very much less clearly defined or even absent in subspecies *A. rhodesiensis rupicolus*.
Legs:	All dark — occasionally a few pale scales at tips of segments.
Abdomen:	Dark but somewhat paler at base of each segment.
Distribution:	Very widely distributed throughout most of Africa south of the Sahara.
Feeding Habits:	Rarely attacks man.
Resting Habits:	Commonly found in caves.
Disease Transmission:	Not important.
Breeding Places:	Found in open (vegetation free) water of all types including rock-pools and footprints either exposed to the sun or shaded.

Note: Adult *Anopheles dthali* can only be separated from *A. rhodesiensis* by the shape and length of the head-scales.

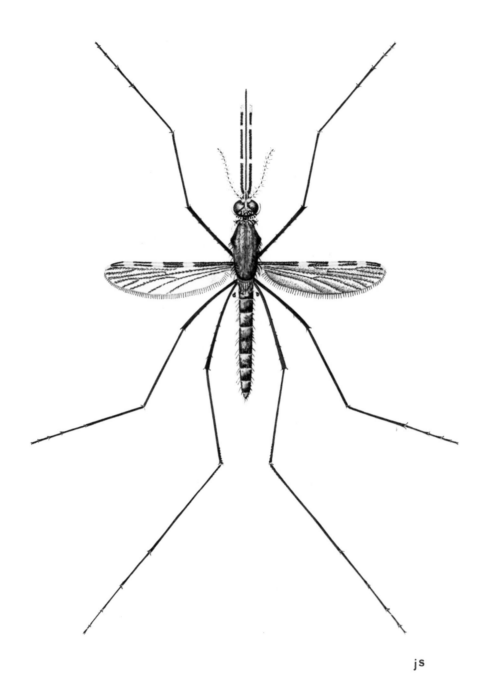

js

15

Anopheles moucheti

Small dark anopheline with two wide pale rings of about equal width at tip of palps. Distinguished from *A. gibbinsi*, *A. hargreavesi*, and *A. marshallii* by absence of pale interruption to 3rd main dark area of vein 1.

Palps: Dark and smooth with three pale rings including one at tip; Ring 1 small, 2 and 3 wide.

Thorax: Grey down centre with creamy scales; dark brown towards edges.

Wings: Pale scales creamy-yellow in colour; two pale interruptions to base of costa; *no pale interruption to 3rd main dark area of vein 1.* Pale fringe spots at tips of all veins except vein 6.

Legs: Long and mainly dark, but with pale tips to all tibiae, and pale tips to most of the tarsal segments (particularly on the front legs).

Abdomen: No scales.

Distribution: Widespread in equatorial regions from Gabon and Nigeria in the west to Uganda.

Feeding Habits: On man, often in houses, mostly by night.

Resting Habits: Commonly found in houses.

Disease Transmission: Important transmitter of human malaria.

Breeding Places: Larvae found in great numbers often associated with water lettuce (*Pistia stratiotes*) along the edges of streams and rivers, very common in the Victoria Nile and Kagera rivers; usually associated with forested regions.

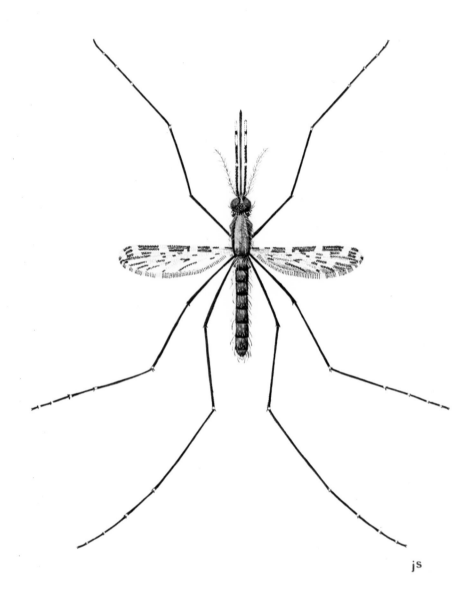

js

Anopheles funestus complex

Small dark anophelines with almost entirely dark legs and three *narrow* white rings to palps. Eight species recognised (*A. funestus, A. aruni, A. brucei, A. confusus, A. fuscivenosus, A. leesoni, A. parensis* and *A. rivulorum*) but difficult to separate as adults.

Palps: Dark and smooth with three narrow white rings including one at tip (the last two rings widely separated in most of the species, but broad and narrowly separated in *A. aruni* and *A. brucei*).

Thorax: Grey down centre; dark brown towards edges (orange-brown in *A. rivulorum*).

Wings: With OR without single pale interruption to base of costa; vein 3 pale in middle OR all dark.

Legs: Usually all dark, but with faint pale tips to the tibiae and occasionally also to the first four tarsal segments.

Abdomen: Dark brown, without scales.

Distribution: *A. funestus, A. leesoni* and *A. rivulorum* widespread throughout much of the continent. *A. aruni* Zanzibar; *A. brucei* Nigeria; *A. parensis* E. Africa; *A. confusus, A. fuscivenosus* Rhodesia.

Feeding Habits: *A. funestus* feeds on man, mainly inside houses by night.

A. aruni and *A. parensis* feed on man, outside houses, by night.

A. leesoni and *A. rivulorum* feed mainly on animals.

Resting Habits: *A. funestus*—mainly inside houses.

A. aruni, A. fuscivenosus, A. leesoni, A. parensis and *A. rivulorum* outside houses.

Disease
Transmission: Malaria — very important (*A. funestus*).

Filaria — important (*A. funestus*).

Viruses — o'nyong-nyong, Bwamba fever, Tanga and Nyando (*A. funestus*).

Breeding Places: Cool, clean shady rivers, streams and pools—often associated with the water lettuce, *Pistia stratiotes*, and grass at edges of rivers; also found in rice; very rarely found in Papyrus swamps or in any water containing red-brown scum.

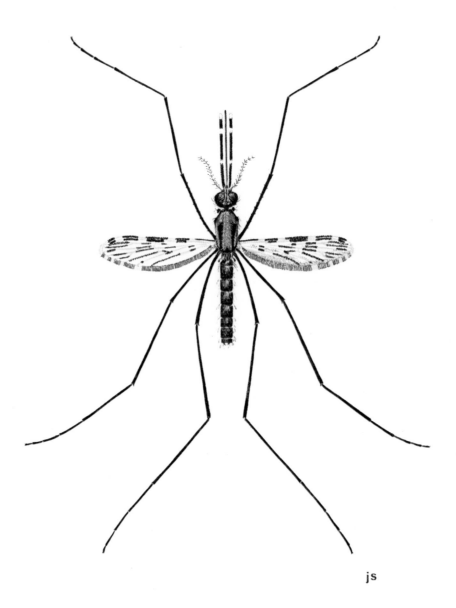

js

19

Anopheles wellcomei

Medium-sized, creamy-yellow anopheline, typically with outer portion of proboscis and palps yellowish.

Palps:	Dark at base; yellowish for outer two-thirds with three pale rings (outer two rings very broad); palps all dark but with three pale rings in subspecies *A. w. ugandae* and intermediate in *A. w. erepens*.
Thorax:	Pale scales on a yellowish background.
Wings:	Costa mainly dark with only two pale interruptions; pale areas markedly yellow.
Legs:	Plain, except for pale bands at tips of some of the tarsal segments.

Front
and $\Big\}$ Tarsi — segments 1–3 pale at tips.
Middle

Hind — Tarsus — segments 1–4 pale at tips, (pale tips to tarsal segments confined to front legs in subspecies *A. w. erepens*).

Abdomen:	Yellowish-brown with pale hairs and no scales.
Distribution:	Widespread in open country (subspecies *A. w. erepens* so far found only in the Pare Taveta region on the Tanzania-Kenya border).
Feeding Habits:	On animals and man, both inside and outside houses mostly by night.
Resting Habits.	Mainly, but not entirely outside.
Disease Transmission:	Important local or occasional transmitter of human malaria.
Breeding Places:	In grassy swamps and rice fields—Larvae and pupae have habit of climbing up the stems of grass, above the water-level (they also climb up the sides of containers when artificially reared); they are thus often difficult to find.

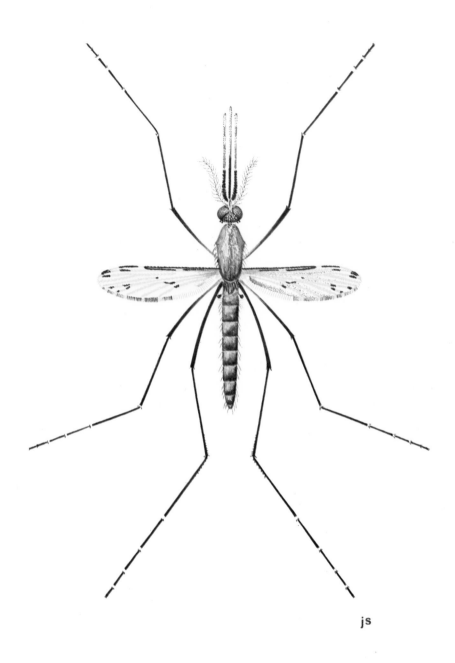

js

21

Anopheles garnhami

Large yellowish brown anopheline found at relatively high altitudes.

Palps:	Smooth with three pale rings including one at the tip; the last two widely separated.
Thorax:	Much of upper surface with a thick covering of creamy-yellow scales.
Wings:	Pale scales creamy-yellow; pale spot in 2nd dark area of vein 1; vein 5 pale at fork.
Legs:	All femora and tibiae with pale rings at tips.
	All tarsi — segments 1–3 with pale rings at tips (few pale scales occasionally present at tip of segment 4).
Abdomen:	No scales.
Distribution:	Found in eastern highlands from Ethiopia to Transvaal, from 1800 to 3300 metres in East Africa to much lower altitudes in the more temperate regions of South Africa.
Feeding Habits:	Occasionally on man, during evenings and night-time.
Resting Habits:	In houses and in cattle-sheds.
Disease Transmission:	Not important.
Breeding Places:	Varied—rock-pools, foot-prints, overgrown ditches, streams, rivers, drains.

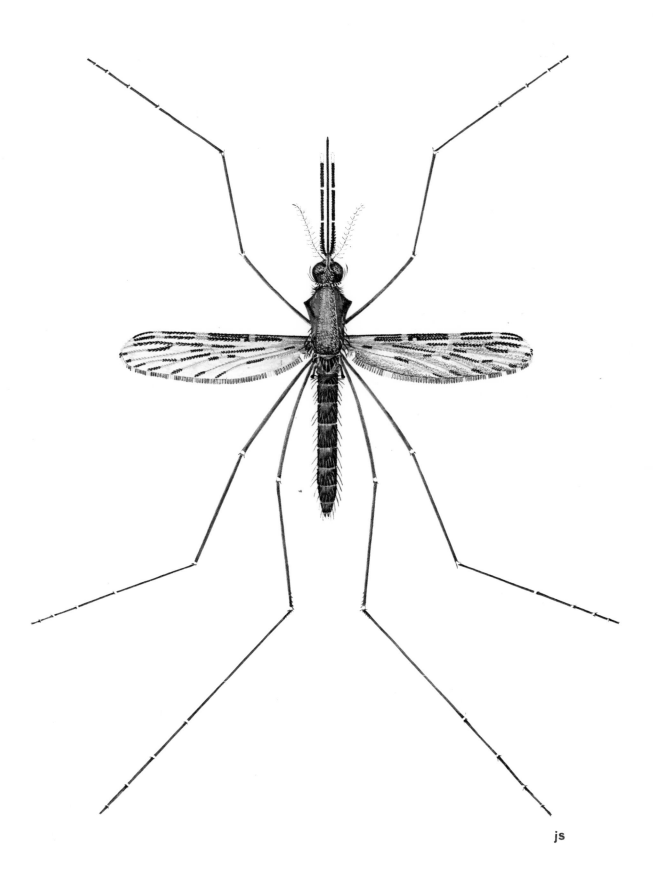

js

23

Anopheles christyi

Large anopheline with four pale rings to the palps.

Palps:	Smooth with four narrow pale rings, including slightly wider ring at tip.
Thorax:	Covered with creamy coloured scales.
Wings:	Pale scales creamy coloured; conspicuous pale fringe-spots at tips of veins 3 to 5.2 and usually 6.
Legs:	All femora and tibiae with narrow line of pale scales along outer side. All tibiae with pale spot at tip. All tarsi — segments 1–4 with conspicuous pale rings; segment 5 all dark.
Abdomen:	Conspicuous yellowish scales down centre of segments 2-8.
Distribution:	East African highlands from Ethiopia to Tanzania, Rwanda and Katanga, occurring from 1400 to 2500 metres.
Feeding Habits:	Mainly on animals but also on man.
Resting Habits:	Cattle-sheds and houses (occasionally present in enormous numbers in houses).
Disease Transmission:	Not normally important.
Breeding Places:	Exposed pools and seepages of many kinds, often in the presence of decaying vegetation.

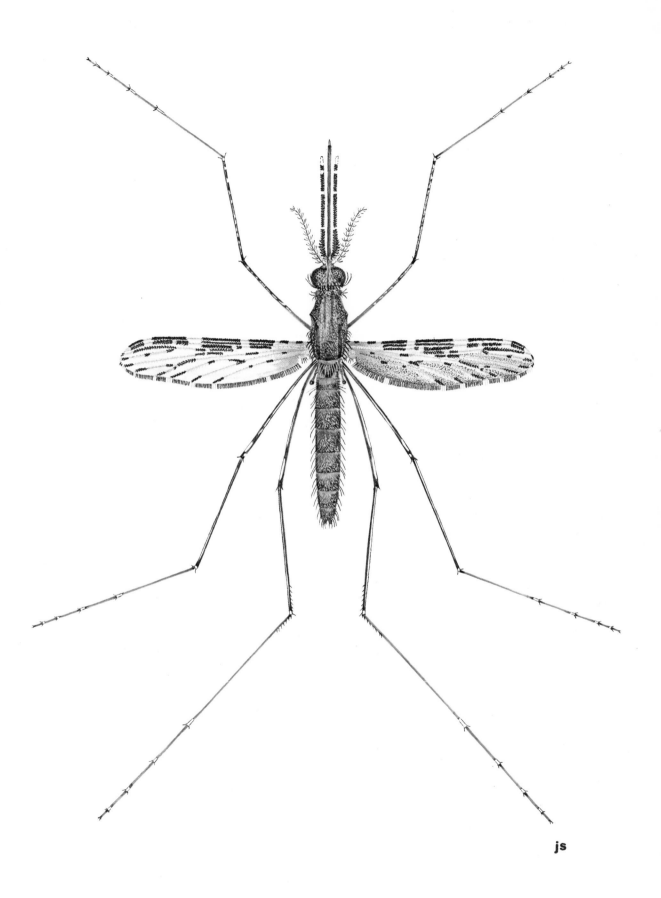

js

Anopheles gambiae

Medium-sized anopheline with irregularly speckled legs, pale spot in 3rd dark area of wing vein 1 and lower branch of vein 5 mostly pale.

Palps: Smooth with three pale rings including wide ring at tip (wide ring at tip occasionally divided into two).

Thorax: Grey, brown, reddish-brown or nearly black, with creamy-yellow scales along centre of back.

Wings: Pale areas very variable in extent (sometimes greatly reduced). Pale scales creamy-yellow; pale patches on costa and vein 1 usually long; two pale onterruptions at base of costa; pale spot in 3rd dark area of vein 1; vein 3 pale except at each end; main branch of vein 5 pale except at each end; fringe-spots present at tips of veins 2-6 (additional fringe-spot between tip of vein 5.2 and 6).

Legs: Irregularly speckled (speckling in some specimens very conspicuous; in others, only just visible).
Tibiae — narrow pale ring at tip.
Tarsi — segments 1-4 pale at tips;
segments 2-4 also pale at bases in front and middle legs (narrower on middle legs).

Abdomen: Pale brown (occasionally much darker) and hairy, often with scales on back of segment 8 and sometimes on segment 7.

Distribution: Very widely distributed (from sea-level to about 2,000 metres in equatorial regions; confined to lower altitudes further south).

Feeding Habits: On man (and animals) by night, mostly indoors.

Resting Habits: Inside and outside houses.

Disease Transmission: Malaria — very important.
Filaria — important.
Viruses — o'nyong-nyong.

Breeding Places: Open exposed (often muddy) ground pools of all sizes; brick-pits, foot-prints, tyre ruts etc. Very occasionally found in man-made containers such as wheelbarrows, mortar-pans etc., and at times of very heavy infestation they have even been found in domestic ant-traps within houses (but this is quite exceptional).

CLOSELY RELATED SPECIES: *A. melas* (West Coast salt-water breeder) is darker than typical
A. gambiae and tends to have four-ringed palps (important vector of malaria along West African coast).

A. merus (East Coast salt-water breeder) also tends to have four-ringed palps.

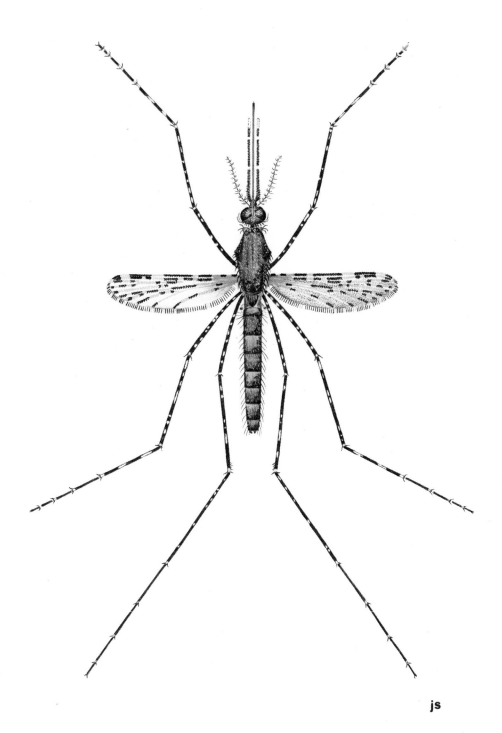

js

Anopheles maculipalpis

Medium-sized anopheline with white-speckled palps and legs and with partly-white hind tarsi.

Palps: Smooth, dark and speckled, with three white rings, including one at tip (the amount of speckling varies).

Thorax: Covered with pale scales, except towards edges.

Wings: Patches of white scales variable in extent; upper branch of vein 5 white at base.

Legs: Speckled or with conspicuous white spots.
Hind tarsi — segment 2 with white outer half;
segments 3-5 all white.

Abdomen: Dark scales on hind edge of segment 8 (pale scales on underside).

Distribution: Widespread, particularly in savanna regions.

Feeding Habits: On animals and occasionally on man, by *night, outside* houses.

Resting Habits: In cattle-sheds etc.

*Disease
Transmission:* Not important.

Breeding Places: Open seepage-pools and other usually exposed places.

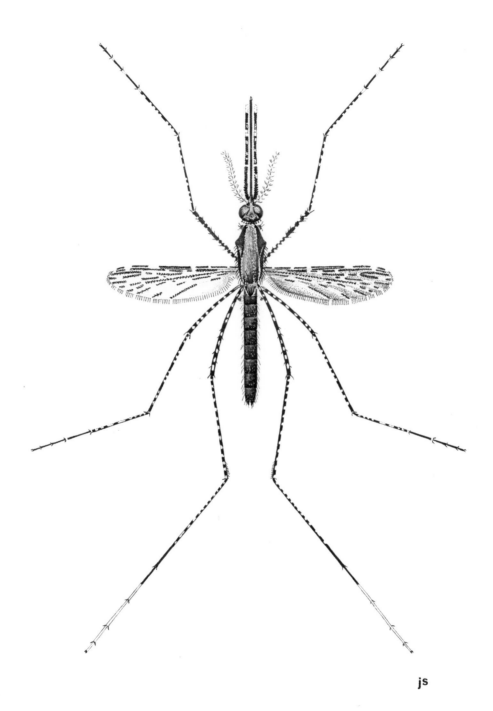

js

29

Anopheles pharoensis

Medium-sized cream-coloured or greyish anopheline with shaggy palps and tufts along each side of abdomen.

Palps: Shaggy, pale brown with four main pale rings including one at the tip.

Thorax: Grey (with white-grey scales); two dark spots towards front.

Wings: Creamy-coloured scales covering most of the wing, except for leading edge (distribution of pale and dark scales variable); sometimes white scales on costa and vein 1.

Legs: All femora and tibiae speckled or with irregular pale patches;
Front
and }— Tarsi — segments 1-3 with pale tips;
Middle   segments 4 and 5 all dark or with very narrow pale tips.
Hind   — Tarsus — segments 1-4 with wide pale tips;
            segment 5 all pale.

Abdomen: Thick covering of yellow or grey scales; conspicuous dark tufts each side of segments 2-7; some white scales on segment 8.

Distribution: Common in nearly all unforested areas from the Nile Delta and Sudan right down to Transvaal; absent from Zanzibar and Pemba; migrates from time to time through forested areas.

Feeding Habits: On animals and man inside houses and outside, mainly at night.

Resting Habits: Mainly outside, among vegetation.

Disease Transmission: Important local or occasional transmitter of human malaria; Sindbis virus has been recovered from this species.

Breeding Places: Mainly swamps, common in grass and other plants both inside and outside the papyrus zone fringing lakes and rivers; also in rice-fields and reservoirs.

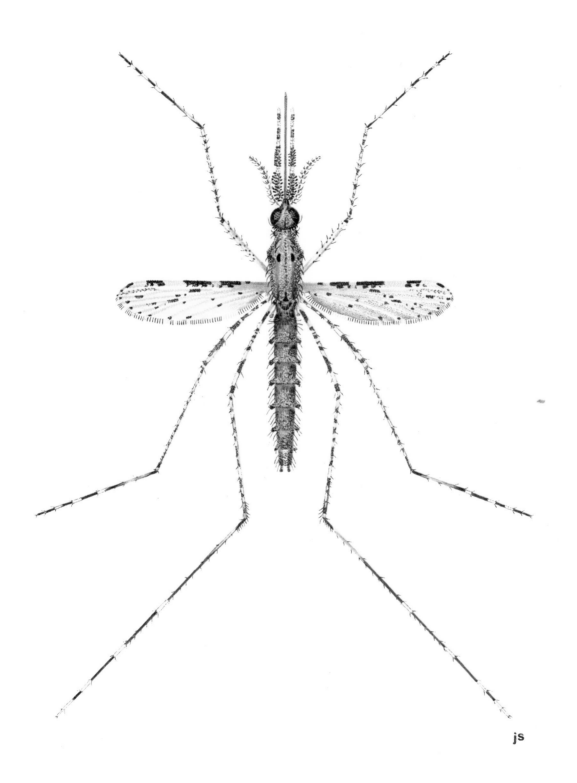

js

31

Anopheles squamosus

Medium-sized anopheline with dark shaggy palps, tufted abdomen and ringed hind tarsi.

Palps: Dark and shaggy with four main white rings including one at tip; some scattered pale scales sometimes present in the dark areas.

Thorax: White scales on a dark grey or black background (sometimes yellowish towards centre); two dark spots near front.

Wings: Base of costa with up to three white interruptions; 3rd main dark area of *vein 1 with white spot;* vein 5 mostly white but dark at fork of upper branch.

Legs: Front — Tibia — white scales in front tending to form white line.
                           Tarsus — segment 1 — scales tending to form white line for much of its length.
                                             segments 1-3 — white at tip.
            Middle — Femur — speckled in front, pale behind.
                         Tibia — white scales in front tending to form white line.
                         Tarsus — segment 1 — scales tending to form white line for much of its length;
                                             segments 1-3 white at tip.
            Hind   — Femur — speckled in front, pale behind.
                         Tibia — white scales in front tending to form white line.
                         Tarsus — as above but segment 1 dark for more than half its length; segments 1-4 white at tip.

Abdomen: Mixture of dark and yellowish scales, particularly towards hind end of each segment; white scales on segment 8; tufts of scales on sides of segments 2-7; underside with white scales.

Distribution: Common throughout tropical Africa (even at fairly high altitudes), Zanzibar and Pemba.

Feeding Habits: Mostly animals but also man, inside and outside houses mainly at night.

Resting Habits: Mainly outside.

Disease
  Transmission: Occasional importance only.

Breeding Places: Seepage-pools, ponds, streams etc. associated with vegetation.

Note: A. *cydippus* and A. *swahilicus* closely resemble A. *squamosus:* A. *cydippus* usually has broader pale bands on the hind tarsus; A. *swahilicus* is very small and has a largely pale upper branch of wing-vein 2.

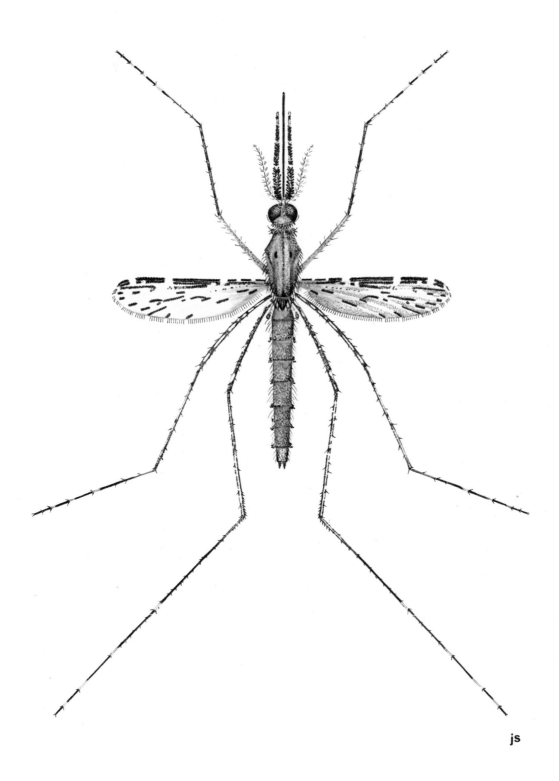

js

Ficalbia flavopicta

Medium-sized, distinctly marked, yellow and brown culicine with rather long palps and pale-banded tarsi.

Head:	Yellow scales on top of head.
Proboscis:	Dark.
Palps:	One-third length of proboscis.
Antennae:	*1st segment very long.*
Thorax:	Wide yellow border; yellow scales tending to form stripes on brown background.
Wings:	Creamy-yellow scales on 1st half of vein 1; otherwise mainly dark.
Legs:	Mainly dark; tibiae with stout bristles; femora and tibiae with yellow tips.

Front
and   — Tarsi — segments 1-4 with narrow pale rings at base.
Middle

Hind   — Tarsus — segments 1-4 with somewhat wider rings at base and extending over tips of preceding segments; segment 5 — pale.

Abdomen:	Dark brown; segments 2-7 with conspicuous inverted v-shaped markings; yellowish lateral spots.
Distribution:	East and central Africa.
Feeding Habits:	Very occasionally on man, in forest, both by day and by night.
Resting Habits:	Not known.
Disease Transmission:	Not important.
Breeding Places:	Not known.

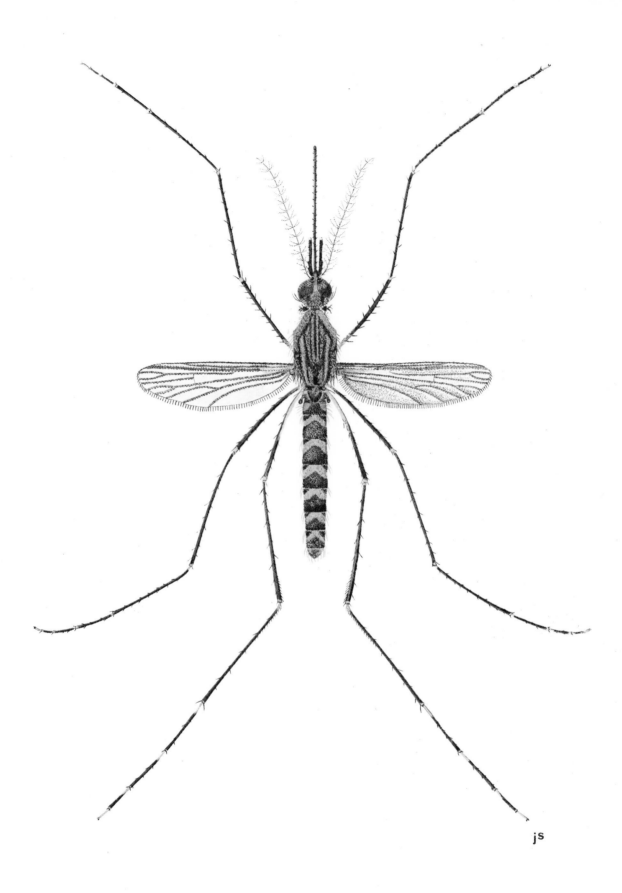

js

Coquillettidia metallica

Large dark metallic-purple culicine with pale scales covering first two-thirds of thorax.

Proboscis:	Dark.
Palps:	Dark.
Thorax:	Mainly dark except for thick covering of first two-thirds by creamy-white scales.
Scutellum:	Some whitish scales on yellowish background.
Wings:	Dark-scaled.
Legs:	Dark or metallic-purple; pale at base of femora.
Abdomen:	Dark blue-purple or violet with small pale spots down each side, particularly noticeable on segments 5-7 (those on 2-4 sometimes inconspicuous).
Distribution:	Very widespread.
Feeding Habits:	On birds and occasionally on man, mostly by day, outside. Feeds extensively in the forest canopy.
Resting Habits:	Very common outside on foliage.
Disease Transmission:	The virus of West Nile fever from bird to bird and probably occasionally from bird to man.
Breeding Places:	The larvae and pupae remain below the water surface attaching themselves to the roots, stems and leaves of plants growing through or floating on the water.

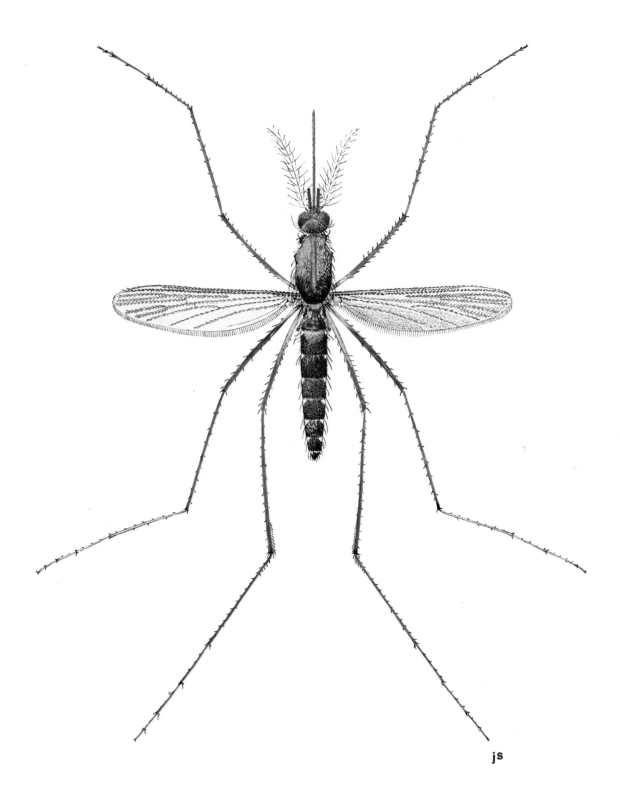

js

Coquillettidia pseudoconopas

A large green and black culicine (turning yellow and black with age) with two dark patches on front end of thorax.

Proboscis:	Green (or yellow) with black tip.
Palps:	Green (or yellow) with black tip.
Thorax:	Green (or yellow) on front two-thirds; dark on hind third; usually with two large dark patches in the green (or yellow) front area; conspicuous dark marks on each side.
Wings:	Mainly yellow-scaled but with patches of dark scales here and there, especially on the forked veins and on vein 6. (In some specimens the dark scales tend to form two distinct stripes from front to back.)
Legs:	Yellow with dark scales on femora and on front of tibiae.

Front
and   }— Tarsi — segments 1-5 black tipped.
Middle

Hind   — Tibia with a narrow black ring near middle and another at tip.
         Tarsus — segments 1-5 with extensive black area at ends.

Abdomen:	Green (or yellow) with dark hind margins to segments 2-6 (segments 2-4 sometimes mainly dark).
Distribution:	Central Africa.
Feeding Habits:	Probably mainly on birds, but quite commonly on man, especially in forest both by day and by night.
Resting Habits:	Very common among foliage.
Disease Transmission:	Probably not important.
Breeding Places:	Larvae and pupae remain below the surface of the water, attaching themselves to the roots, stems and leaves of certain plants growing through or floating on the water.

Note: Parasitic mites very common.

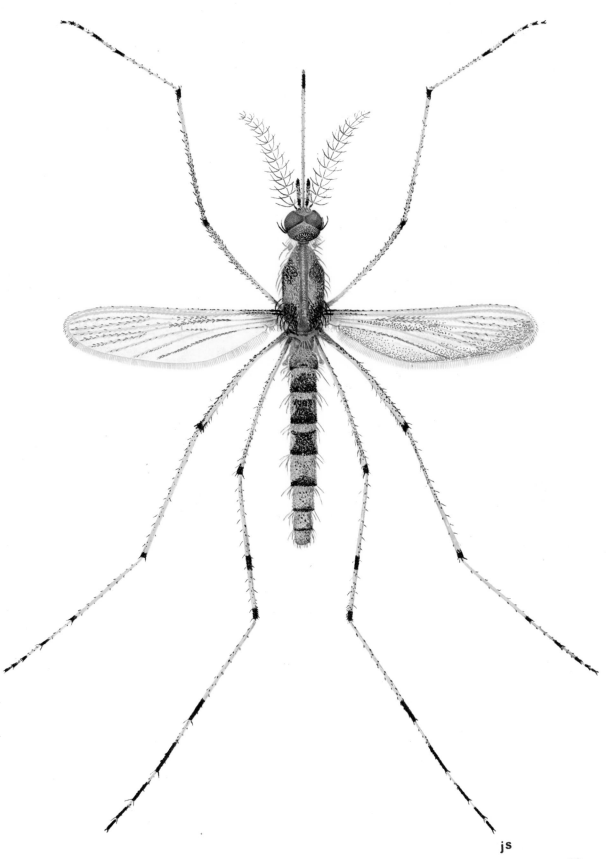

js

39

Coquillettidia maculipennis

Medium-sized green and black culicine (turning yellow and black with age) with pale yellow scales on front end of thorax.

Proboscis:	Green (or yellow) with black tip.
Palps:	Green (or yellow) with black tip.
Thorax:	Green (or yellow) with metallic pale yellow scales on front two thirds. Dark stripe across each side.
Wings:	Yellow with patches of dark scales tending to form two distinct broad stripes from front to back (this feature is sometimes absent).
Legs:	Yellow with dark scales on femora and on front of tibiae.

Front and Middle — Tarsi — segments 1-5 black tipped.

Hind — Tibia — with a narrow black ring near middle and another at tip.
Tarsus — segment 1 — with black tip;
segments 2-4 — black for final third to one-half;
segment 5 — nearly all black.

Abdomen:	Green (or yellow) with conspicuous dark hind margin to segments 2-6.
Distribution:	Very widely distributed from Sudan to Transvaal and from Nigeria to Tanzania.
Feeding Habits:	Quite commonly on man especially in forest, both by day and by night.
Resting Habits:	Very common among foliage.
Disease Transmission:	Probably not important.
Breeding Places:	Larvae and pupae remain below the surface of the water, attaching themselves to the roots, stems and leaves of certain plants growing through or floating on the water.

Note: C. *maculipennis* is very similar to the mainly West African C. *annettii* but may usually be distinguished by the two bands of dark scales on the wings and by the dark stripe across each side of the thorax.

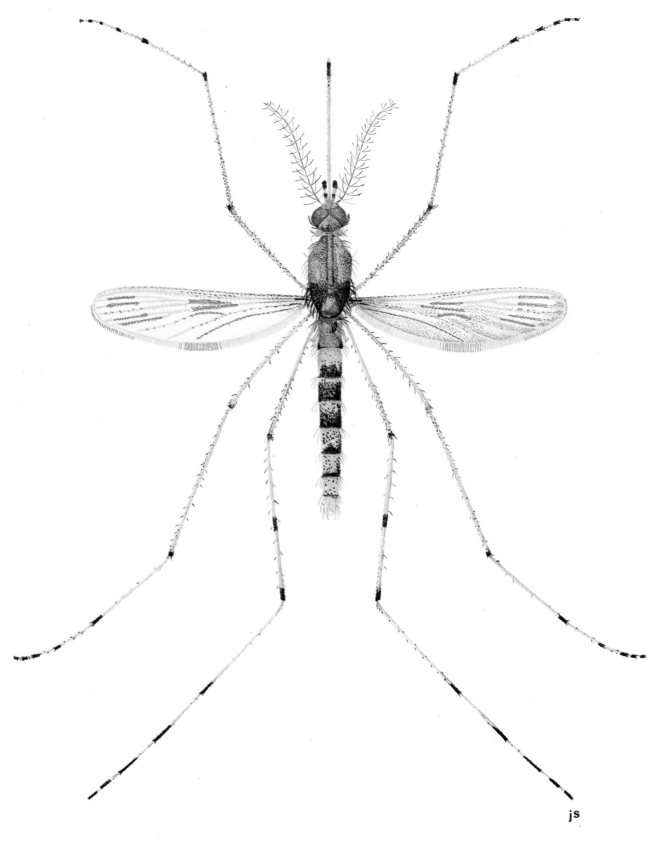

js

41

Coquillettidia fuscopennata

Large brown and yellow culicine with yellow and black legs.

Proboscis:	Yellow with black tip.
Palps:	Yellow with some black scales at tip.
Thorax:	Yellowish-brown (sometimes very dark brown especially towards the sides).
Scutellum:	Yellow without scales.
Wings:	Costa with many yellow scales; dark and yellow scales on other veins.
Legs:	Yellow with many black scales on femora and on front and middle tibiae.

Front
and   }— Tarsi   — segments 1-3 black tipped.
Middle

Hind   — Tibia with black ring near middle and another at tip.
Tarsus — segments 1-3 black at ends;
segment 4 — black or mostly black;
segment 5 — all black.

Abdomen:	Covered with dark and yellow scales.
Distribution:	Very common particularly in East and Central Africa wherever there are extensive swamps; the numbers increase enormously following a rise in swamp or lake-level after heavy rains.
Feeding Habits:	Persistent feeder on man, particularly at night but occasionally also on a dull day; feeds both inside houses and outside. In swampy areas it can be one of the worst pest-species, feeding on man, dog and other animals, including frogs and toads.
Resting Habits:	Inside and outside houses.
Disease Transmission:	The following viruses have been recovered from *C. fuscopennata*: chikungunya, Rift Valley fever and Sindbis.
Breeding Places:	In swamps—the larvae and pupae live in the mud at the bottom, attaching themselves to the roots of plants that are growing in the water.

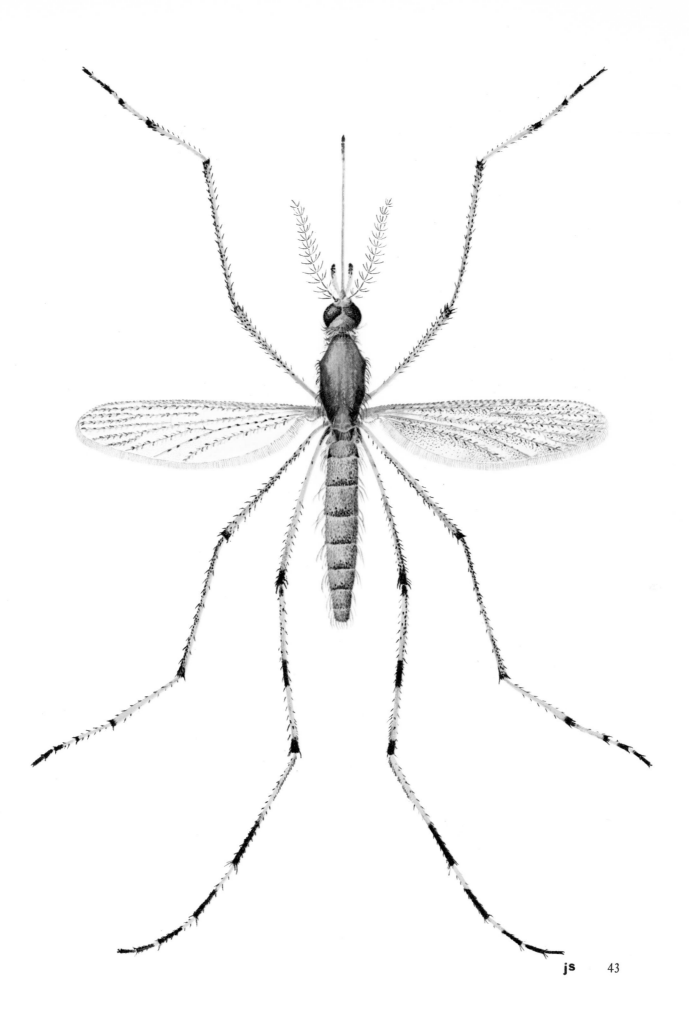

Coquillettidia aurites

Large golden-yellow culicine with black ring near middle of hind tibia.

Proboscis: Yellow with black tip.

Palps: Yellow, sometimes with a few black scales at tip.

Thorax: Metallic golden-yellow.

Wings: Yellow with a few dark scales sometimes present, especially on vein 6.

Legs: Yellow with some scattered black scales on all femora and on front and middle tibiae.
All femora yellow at the tip.
Front   — Tarsus yellow with black tips (segments 3-5 often all dark).
Middle — Tarsus mainly yellow (5 sometimes all dark).
Hind   — Tibia with black ring near middle and another at tip.
             Tarsus — segment 1 yellow with black tip extending from one-sixth to as much as one-third the length of the segment;
                     segments 2 and 3 black outer half (segment 3 nearly all black in some specimens);
                     segments 4 and 5 all black.

Abdomen: Mainly yellow but often with black scales on segments 2-4 tending to form triangular patches. *No black dot on hind corners of segment 1.*

Distribution: Widely distributed throughout much of tropical Africa from West to East.

Feeding Habits: Mainly on birds in the forest canopy by night. Occasionally on man in forest and plantation by day.

Resting Habits: Mainly on foliage but occasionally in houses.

Disease Transmission: Usutu virus has been recovered from this species.

Breeding Places: Almost any collection of water with plants growing through or floating on the water; the larvae remain below the surface, attaching themselves to the stems, roots, and leaves of the plants.

Note: C. aurites is very closely related to C. aurea and C. microannulata; C. aurea is distinguished by a yellow ring at base of segment 4 of hind tarsus and by few or no black scales on abdomen.
C. micrannulata is almost entirely yellow with no black ring in middle of hind tibia.
Intergrades occur and in my opinion *aurea* and *microannulata* should be regarded as subspecies of C. *aurites:*
        C. *aurites aurites*
        C. *aurites aurea*
        C. *aurites microannulata*

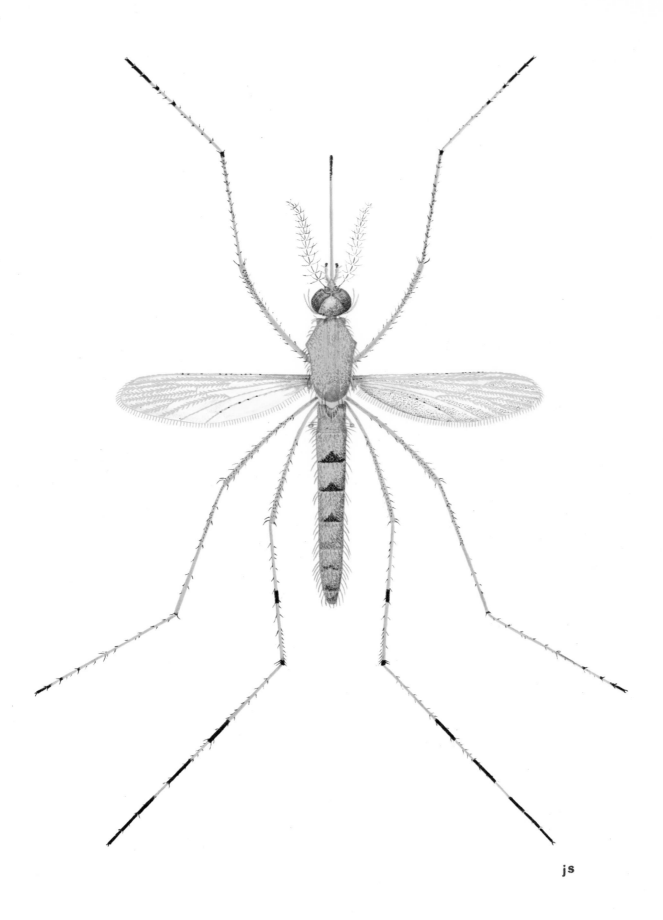

js

45

Coquillettidia fraseri

Medium-sized golden-yellow culicine resembling *C. aurites* but with black tips to all femora, and a black spot on the hind corners of the first abdominal segment.

Proboscis: Yellow with black tip.

Palps: Yellow usually with some black scales at tip.

Thorax: Metallic golden yellow.

Wings: Yellow with a few dark scales, especially on vein 6.

Legs: Yellow with scattered black scales on all femora and tibiae, particularly so on front surface of middle tibia.
All femora with distinct black ring at tip.
Front — Tarsus — segments 1-3 yellow with black tips.
Middle — Tarsus — mainly yellow except for segment 5; segments 2-4 with narrow black tips.
Hind — Tarsus — segment 1 yellow with black tip for variable length; segments 2 and 3 black at least for outer half; segments 4 and 5 all black.

Abdomen: Mainly yellow, but usually with black scales on segments 2-4 tending to form triangular patches. *A black dot on hind corners of segment 1.*

Distribution: East and Central Africa (probably more widely distributed than records indicate).

Feeding Habits: Probably mainly on birds—occasionally on man by night and sometimes by day in forest.

Resting Habits: Among vegetation.

Disease Transmission: Nothing yet known.

Breeding Places: Swamps and pools with grass and other plants growing in and on the water; the larvae and pupae remain below the water surface, attaching themselves to the stems, roots and leaves of plants.

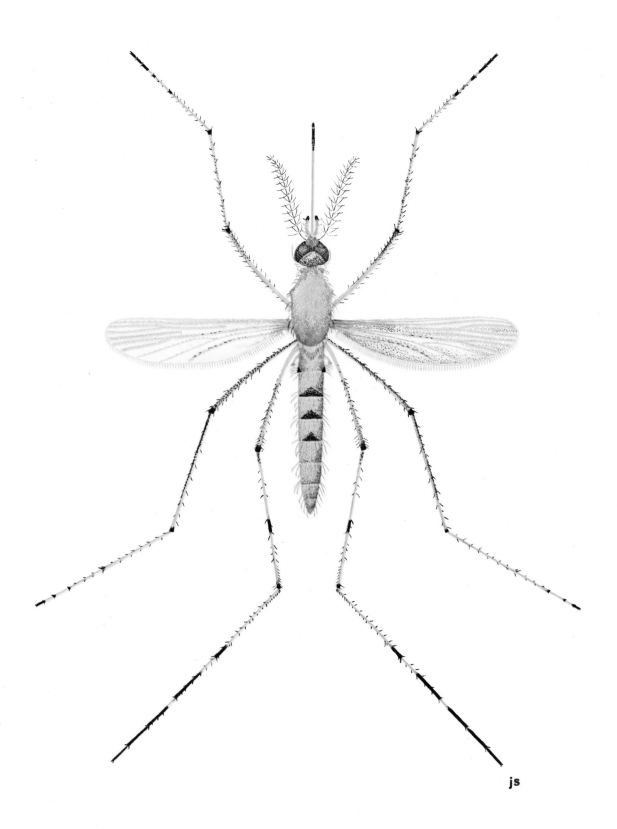

js

47

Mansonia uniformis

Medium-sized, very scaly culicine with six pale rings on hind tarsi and extensive but poorly defined pale area on front surface of hind femora and tibiae.

Proboscis:	Yellow ring in middle and yellow scales at tip.
Palps:	Dark with pale tip.
Thorax:	Variable pattern of brown, grey-green and yellowish scales tending to form a pattern of lengthwise stripes.
Wings:	Covered almost equally by large brown and large yellow scales.
Legs:	Hind — Femur and tibia — *front surface extensively pale for first half.* Tarsus with six pale rings.
Abdomen:	Dark brown with central patches of creamy scales on segments 1-2 or 3; segment 7 nearly all white.
Distribution:	Very common and widely spread in most of Africa south of the Sahara. Also occurs in Asia, the Pacific and in northern Australia.
Feeding Habits:	Very common feeder on man, both inside and outside houses, mainly by night.
Resting Habits:	Very common inside houses.
Disease Transmission:	The following viruses have been recovered from *M. uniformis:* Bwamba fever, chikungunya, Ndumu, Rift Valley fever, Spondweni and Wesselsbron. This species is also a common transmitter of filarial worms (leading sometimes to elephantiasis).
Breeding Places:	Swamps of all kinds associated with vegetation; the larvae and pupae remain below the surface of the water, attaching themselves to the roots, stems and leaves of plants.

Note: M. uniformis and M. africana are very much alike, and intermediates are found as far as the thoracic markings are concerned. The females are most easily separated by examining the front side of the hind femora (the appearance is clearly shown in plates 23 and 24, in which the hind femora have been shown deliberately with the markings of the front surface).

Young adults of both species often infested by red parasitic mites.

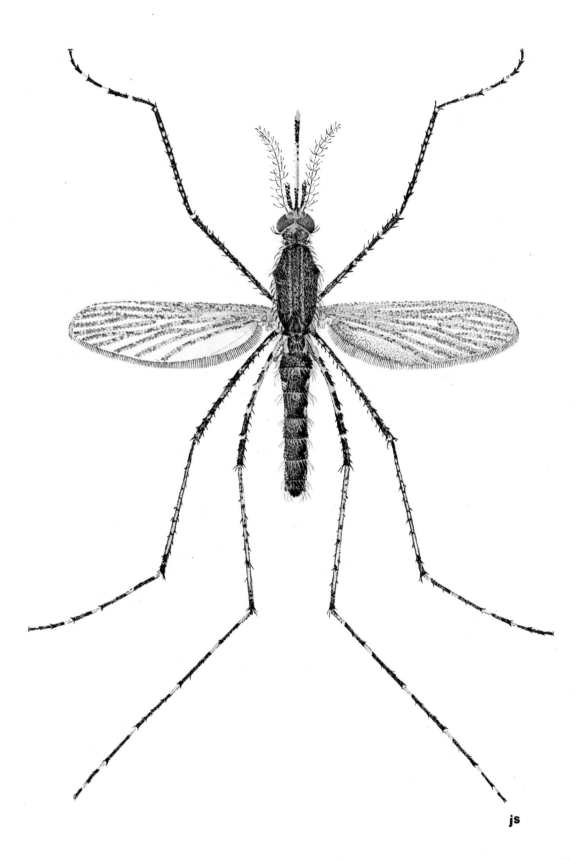

Mansonia africana

Medium-sized, very scaly culicine with six white rings on hind tarsi and clearly defined dark and pale patches on front of femora and tibiae.

Proboscis:	Wide yellow ring in middle and yellow scales at tip.
Palps:	Mainly dark with white tip.
Thorax:	Variable pattern of brown, grey-green and yellowish scales often forming a large rectangular yellowish brown patch.
Wings:	Covered almost equally by large brown and large yellow scales.
Legs:	All femora and tibiae dark brown (or black) with *five or six distinct white patches on front surface.* Hind — Tarsi — with six white rings.
Abdomen:	Dark brown (almost black in specimens from some regions) with central patches of creamy scales on segments 1-2 or 1-3; segment 7 with very white scales.
Distribution:	Very common in most of Africa south of the Sahara.
Feeding Habits:	Very common feeder on man, both inside and outside houses mainly by night.
Resting Habits:	Very common inside houses.
Disease *Transmission:*	The following viruses have been recovered from or transmitted by *M. africana*: Bunyamwera, Bwamba fever, chikungunya, Pongola, Rift Valley fever, Sindbis, Spondweni and yellow fever. This species is also a transmitter of filarial worms (leading sometimes to elephantiasis).
Breeding Places:	Swamps of all kinds associated with vegetation; the larvae and pupae remain below the surface of the water, attaching themselves to the roots, stems and leaves of plants.

Note: See note at end of previous species.

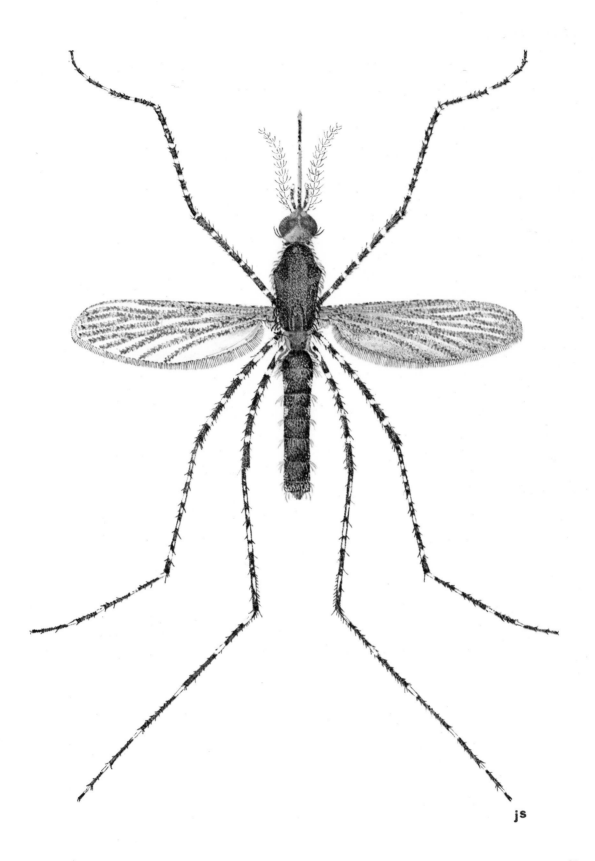

js

Hodgesia spp.

A genus of very small, midge-like, black and silver-white culicines consisting of four species, the females of which cannot easily be distinguished: *H. sanguinae, H. psectropus, H. nigeriae, H. cyptopus.*

Head:	Central silver-white spot.
Palps:	Very short.
Thorax:	Dark with patches of silver scales on each side.
Scutellum:	Scales all dark (no silvery scales).
Wings:	Dark-scaled; those on leading edge and at wing-tip long and notched giving the wing a somewhat shaggy appearance.
Legs:	*Highly modified in males:* End segments of middle tarsi bend sharply down in all four species.
	♂ *H. psectropus:* Tip of front tarsi with single claw and very large brush-like structure called the empodium.
	♂ *H. cyptopus:* Tip of middle tarsi long (bent down) and covered by very long scales from segments 3 and 4.
	♂ *H. sanguinae:* Tip of hind tarsi (segments 4 and 5) greatly enlarged.
	♂ *H. nigeriae:* Bent tips to middle tarsi only.
Abdomen:	Dark with lateral silver-white spots on hind edges of all segments except 3 and 7 (a few white scales occasionally present on segment 3 in *H. sanguinae;* abdominal spots tend to be yellowish and present on segments 1-6 inclusive, in *H. cyptopus*).
Distribution:	Widely distributed in tropical Africa.
Feeding Habits:	On man (and probably on other vertebrates) in forest and occasionally in houses.
Resting Habits:	Among foliage and occasionally in houses.
Disease Transmission:	Not known.
Breeding Places:	Swamps, including papyrus.

Note: The genus *Malaya*, consisting of eight species of very small black and silver-white mosquitos (without silver spots on abdominal segment 3), can be separated from *Hodgesia* by the swollen tip of the proboscis, the silver-white scales on the scutellum, and (in the males) by the unmodified tarsi.

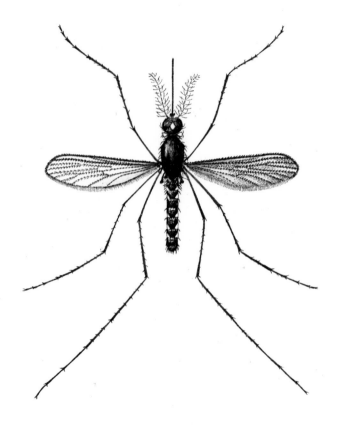

js

Aedeomyia furfurea

Small very scaly dark culicine with speckled wings and banded legs.

Proboscis: Dark with two wide white rings.

Palps: Dark with white scales at middle and tip.

Antennae: Short with few hairs; tips tending to curl round in a complete circle in living specimens.

Thorax: Very scaly with narrow central stripe of yellow scales on front half.
Patch of white scales in front of scutellum.

Scutellum: Some white scales on all three lobes and tuft of black scales at tip of each lobe.

Wings: Almost completely covered with large brown, white and yellow scales; few or no yellow scales at base of wing; white spot on outer half of vein 3.

Legs: Rather thick with tufts of upstanding scales at tips of femora (particularly middle and hind).

     All legs — Femora and Tibiae — brown with many white spots and rings.

     Hind — Tarsus — conspicuous white rings involving joints 1-2 and 2-3; segments 3 and 4 — first third white; segment 5 — nearly all white.

Abdomen: Dark with some white scales along sides and on underside.

Distribution: Mainly East African but extending westward to Cameroun and southward to Natal.

Feeding Habits: Occasionally on man, mainly outside houses by night.

Disease Transmission: Not important.

Breeding Places: Swamps, overgrown borrow-pits, and other places with vegetation growing in the water.

CLOSELY RELATED SPECIES: *A. africana* (mainly West African, but extending eastward to Uganda, Kenya, and Tanzania and southward to Natal).

Proboscis — with three narrow white rings.

Thorax — with large rectangular patch of yellow scales; no scales in front of scutellum.

Scutellum — mostly white.

Wings — yellow scales at base of wing.

Note: Intermediate forms have been recorded and it is difficult to assign some specimens definitely to one or the other. Perhaps *furfurea* should be regarded as an eastern subspecies of *A. africana*.

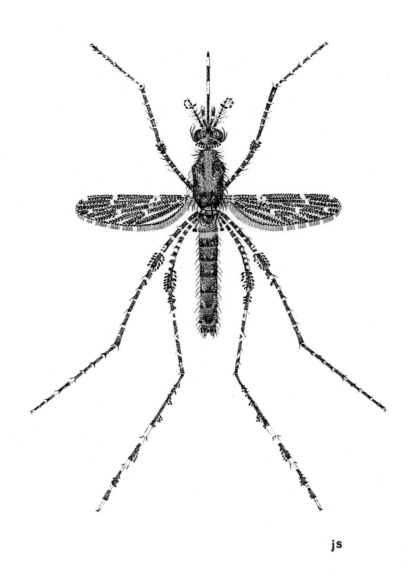

js

Eretmapodites chrysogaster group

Medium to large, slender culicines with silver-white and golden-yellow markings.

Head:	Large patch of silver-white scales between the widely separated eyes and extending backward.
Proboscis:	Dark, long and usually very slightly down-curved.
Palps:	Dark.
Thorax:	Covered by a mixture of yellow and black scales without any obvious pattern (except for occasional presence of a single yellow line in front of scutellum).
Scutellum:	Dark with central stripe of silver-white scales and with yellow scales on outer lobes.
Wings:	Dark-scaled.
Legs:	Long and mainly black.
	Hind — Femur — dark with small white spot at tip; yellow for first two-thirds of outer side only.
Abdomen:	Very narrow (laterally compressed). Black with silver-white markings above and largely golden-yellow beneath.
	Tergite 1 — with two small silver-white spots.
	Tergites 2-7 with large oblique silver-white patches of scales.
	Tergite 8 — partially covered with silver-white scales.
Distribution:	Widely distributed throughout equatorial region.
Feeding Habits:	Very common on man in forests, plantations and other wooded areas, mainly by day.
Resting Habits:	On forest vegetation.
Disease Transmission:	Rift Valley fever virus; also capable of transmitting yellow fever virus. Nkolbisson and Okola viruses have also been recovered from *E. chrysogaster* group.
Breeding Places:	In fallen leaves, fallen bracts of banana flowers, and in snail-shells.

Note: *E. chrysogaster* belongs to a group of 12 species which can be divided into two sub-groups, in each of which the females cannot be separated:

E. chrysogaster, *E. haddowi*, *E. harperi*, *E. intermedius*, *E. mahaffyi*, *E. semisimplicipes*, *E. subsimplicipes* and *E. vansomerenae* all have a pale line on the underside of the proboscis.

E. gilletti, *E. grahami*, *E. mattinglyi* and *E. pauliani* have no pale line on the proboscis.

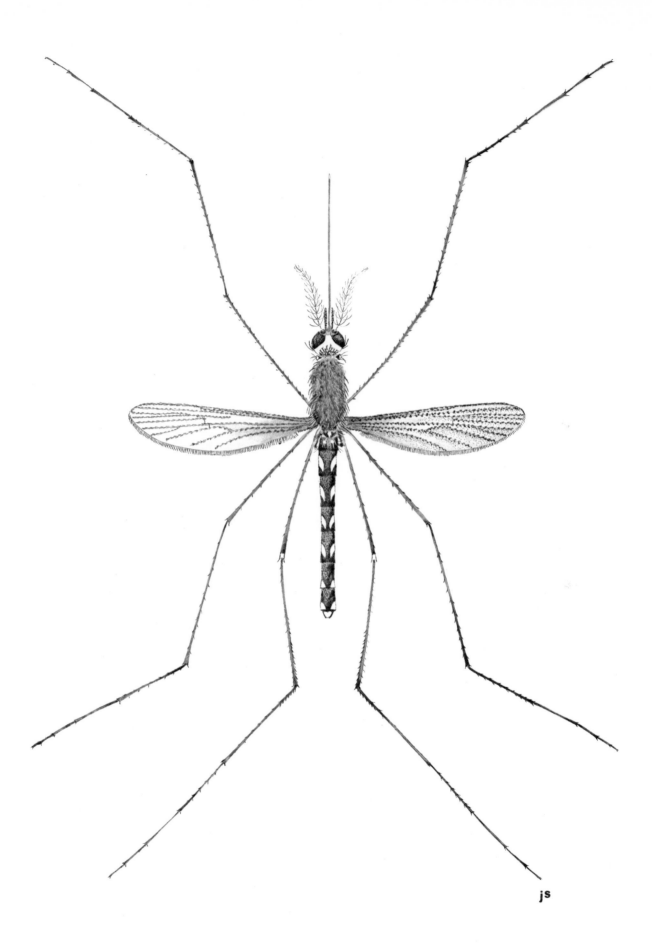

js

Eretmapodites inornatus group

Medium-sized slender culicines with silver-white and golden-yellow markings; a pattern of yellow lines on thorax.

Head:	Large patch of silver-white scales between the widely separated eyes and extending backward.
Proboscis:	Dark, long and usually very slightly down-curved.
Palps:	Dark; one-fifth as long as proboscis.
Thorax:	Dark with narrow yellow border and lines of yellow scales on front two-thirds and a central yellow line on hind one-third.
Scutellum:	Dark with central stripe of silver-white scales and with yellow scales on outer lobes.
Wings:	Dark-scaled.
Legs:	Long and mainly black. Hind — Femur — black for most of its length except for small white spot at tip.
Abdomen:	Narrow (laterally compressed). Black with silver-white above and largely golden-yellow beneath. Tergite 1 with two small silver-white spots. Tergites 2-6 with large oblique patches of silver-white scales; Tergite 7 also with two widely separated silver-white patches.
Distribution:	Central equatorial regions: eastern Congo and western Uganda.
Feeding Habits:	On man in shaded and forested areas, mainly by day.
Resting Habits:	On vegetation.
Disease Transmission:	Not important.
Breeding Places:	Snail shells, fallen leaves and axils of *Colocasia* (cocoyams).

Note: The *inornatus* group includes five closely related species, the females of which are hard to separate: E. *argyrus*, E. *forcipulatus*, E. *inornatus*, E. *melanopus*, and E. *penicillatus*.

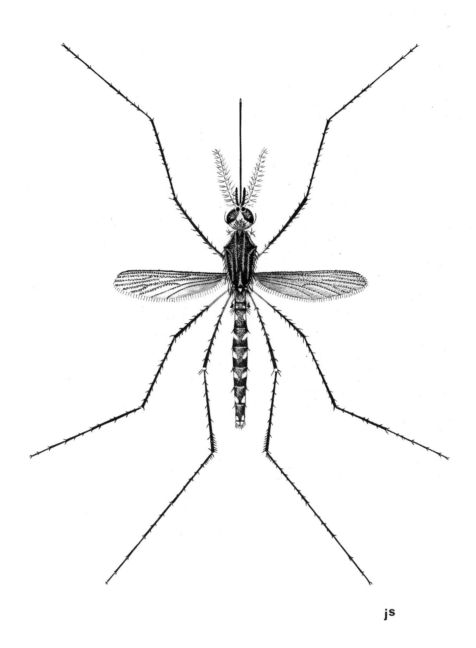

js

59

Eretmapodites quinquevittatus

Medium to large, slender culicine with silver-white and golden-yellow markings; bright yellow and black stripes on thorax.

Head:	Large patch of silver-white scales between the widely separated eyes and extending backward.
Proboscis:	Dark, long and usually very slightly down-curved.
Palps:	Dark.
Thorax:	Five more or less parallel yellow stripes on a dark background.
Scutellum:	Dark with central stripe of silver-white scales and yellow scales on outer lobes.
Wings:	Dark-scaled.
Legs:	Long and mainly black. Femora yellow near base.
Abdomen:	Narrow (laterally compressed). Black and silver-white above and largely golden-yellow beneath. Tergite 1 with two small silver-white spots. Tergite 2-6 with narrow oblique silver-white markings. Tergite 7 usually with these markings joining to form a complete silver-white band. Tergite 8 — often largely covered with silver-white scales.
Distribution:	Very widely distributed throughout much of the African region, including Madagascar.
Feeding Habits:	Common on man, outside houses by day.
Resting Habits:	On vegetation.
Disease *Transmission:*	Not known to be important.
Breeding Places:	Snail shells, leaf axils (banana and pineapple) and sometimes from old tins and bottles.

CLOSELY RELATED SPECIES: *E. dracaenae* (from Ghana, Sierra Leone and eastwards as far as Uganda) and *E. hightoni* (from Uganda and western Kenya) may be separated from *E. quinquevittatus* by the following:

Abdomen — Tergite 1 all dark above (without silver-white spots).
Tergite 2-7 with larger silver-white markings, sometimes forming silver band across tergite.
Tergite 8 with yellow or copper-coloured scales (not silver-white); this segment is often very small (contracted inwards) and not so easily seen as 2-7.

E. corbeti and *E. tonsus* differ from the above by the presence of narrow yellow lines on the thorax (as in *E. inornatus*).
E. tonsus has silver-white markings on first abdominal tergite; *E. corbeti* has no such lines.

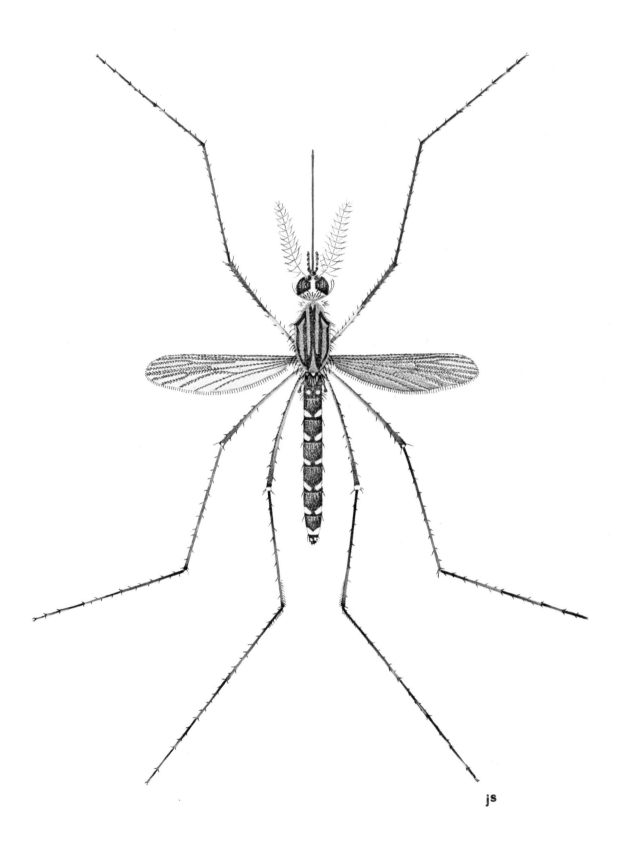

js

Aedes (Finlaya) longipalpis

Small to medium-sized culicine with central silver-white double stripe on thorax and with metallic-blue-black abdomen and legs.

Proboscis:	Dark.
Palps:	Thickly covered in scales; dark and one-third length of proboscis.
Thorax:	Black with central silver-white double stripe running full length of thorax and separating to form a fork shortly before scutellum.
Scutellum:	Silver-white fork extending across outer edges of middle lobe, which is otherwise dark scaled.
Wings:	Short with black scales.
Legs:	Metallic-blue to black.

     Middle — Femur — a silver-white patch in middle *in front*.
                Tarsus — segment 1 — narrow white ring at base;
                                 segment 2 — mostly white.
     Hind — Femur — a silver-white patch in middle *in front*.
                Tibia — pale at base *beneath*.
                Tarsus — segment 1 — narrow white ring at base;
                                 segment 2 — mostly white.

Abdomen:	Pointed at tip; metallic-blue-black, segments 1-6 with silver-white patches towards front edges; two additional silver-white spots near middle of segments 6 and 7; segment 8 mainly silver-white.
Distribution:	West Africa and extending to Congo and Uganda.
Feeding Habits:	Mostly monkeys, in forest trees by day.
Resting Habits:	In trees.
Disease Transmission:	Possible transmitter of Uganda S. virus (and perhaps yellow fever to monkeys).
Breeding Places:	Tree-holes.

CLOSELY RELATED SPECIES: *A. longipalpis* (mainly of W. Africa) closely resembles *A. fulgens* (of East Africa); *A. fulgens* can be separated by the following points:

    Palps—Two-thirds length of proboscis.

    Double silver-white stripe on thorax does *not* fork but widens out in front of scutellum.

    Central lobe of scutellum silver-white.

    Pair of central silver-white spots on segment 5, as well as 6 and 7 of abdomen.

    Hind tibia all dark; middle tarsus—segment 1 nearly all white above; hind tarsus—segment 1 all dark.

    A. mzooi (from Tanzania) differs from both the above species by having the hind femur covered with shining silver-white scales on basal two-thirds in front.

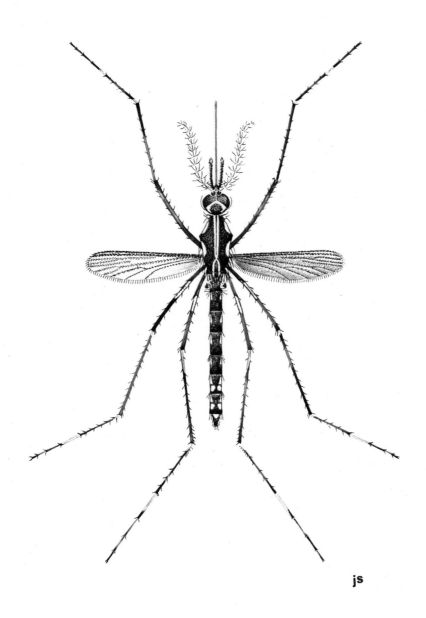

js

Aedes (Finlaya) ingrami

Small to medium-sized culicine with extensive area of creamy scales on front half of thorax extending backwards in a series of stripes.

Head:	Creamy-white with two dark patches.
Proboscis:	Dark.
Palps:	Dark; about one-quarter length of proboscis.
Thorax:	Variable with creamy-white scales in front extending backwards in irregular and somewhat variable pattern, with creamy stripes alternating with black.
Wings:	Dark-scaled.
Legs:	Middle — Femur — basal half of inner surface mainly black. Tarsus — segments 1 and 2 white at base (segment 2 white for at least half its length). Hind — Femur — all white on first half and a white ring near the tip. Tarsus — segments 1 and 2 white at base (segment 2 white for at least half its length).
Abdomen:	Pointed at tip; black with white patches towards outer edges of segments; two additional white spots near centre of segments 6 and 7 (tending to coalesce). Base of segments white on underside.
Distribution:	Widely distributed from Ghana to Kenya and from Sudan to Malawi.
Feeding Habits:	Mainly in the forest canopy just before sunset.
Resting Habits:	In trees.
Disease Transmission:	Suspected transmitter of Uganda S virus.
Breeding Places:	In tree holes.

CLOSELY RELATED SPECIES:
A. *wellmani* (from Angola).
    Middle — Femur — basal half all white on inner surface.
A. *embuensis* (from parts of Kenya).
    Top of head all white.
    Thorax with yellow scales on front portion.
A. *nyasae* (from Malawi).
    Top of head all white.
    Thorax with pair of black lines reaching front edge.
    Legs with metallic gloss (like those of A. *longipalpis*).
    Front tibia all dark.
    Front tarsus with two white rings.
    Hind tarsus with white tip.

Note: My own view is that all these forms should be considered as geographical subspecies: A. *ingrami ingrami;* A. *i. wellmani;* A. *i. embuensis;* A. *i. nyasae.*

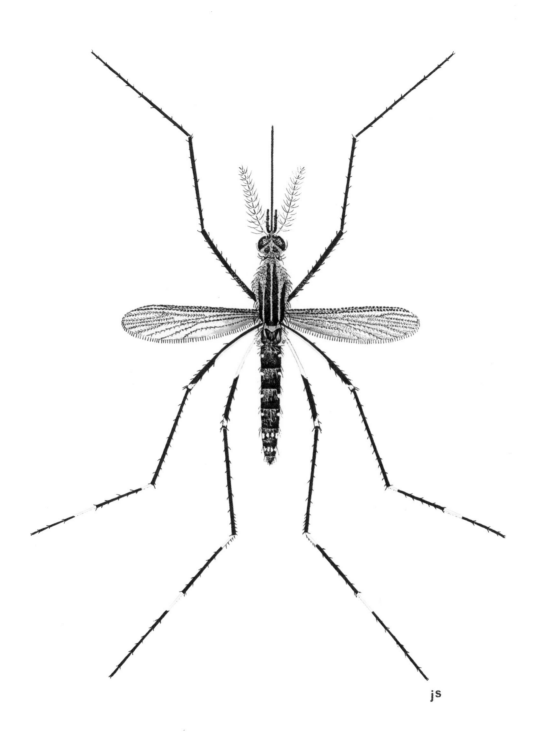

js

Aedes (Finlaya) pulchrithorax

Small to medium-sized culicine with three yellow lines on dark thorax.

Head: Central yellow stripe which continues backwards down the thorax.

Proboscis: Dark.

Palps: Dark, nearly one-third length of proboscis.

Thorax: Black with three distinct yellow lines, the middle line continuing from the head and forking just in front of the scutellum.

Scutellum: With small patch of yellow scales on middle lobe.

Wings: Dark-scaled.

Legs:

Front — Femur — all black above.
Tibia — white line behind.
Tarsus — segment 1 with narrow white ring at base near tip.

Middle — Femur — first half white underneath and short white line near tip.
Tibia — narrowly white at base.
Tarsus — segment 1 with narrow white ring at base; segment 2 with first half all white.

Hind — Femur — first half creamy-white except for black line near tip.
Tibia — broadly white at base behind.
Tarsus — segment 1 with narrow white ring at base; segment 2 with first half all white.

Abdomen: Pointed at tip; black with silver-white basal spots near each side.

Distribution: Highlands of eastern and central Africa.

Feeding Habits: Not known.

Resting Habits: Not known.

Disease
Transmission: Not important.

Breeding Places: Tree-holes and bored-bamboos.

CLOSELY RELATED AND SIMILAR LOOKING SPECIES: Closely resembles *A. hancocki* (from Tanzania).

A. hancocki differs from *A. pulchrithorax* by having the two outer yellow lines on the thorax broader than its middle line.

A. barnardi and *Culex pulchrithorax* (both from South Africa) differ from *A. pulchrithorax* by the almost continuous pale border to the thorax.

C. pulchrithorax is also easily separated by its all-dark tarsi and round-tipped abdomen (typical of most *Culex*).

66

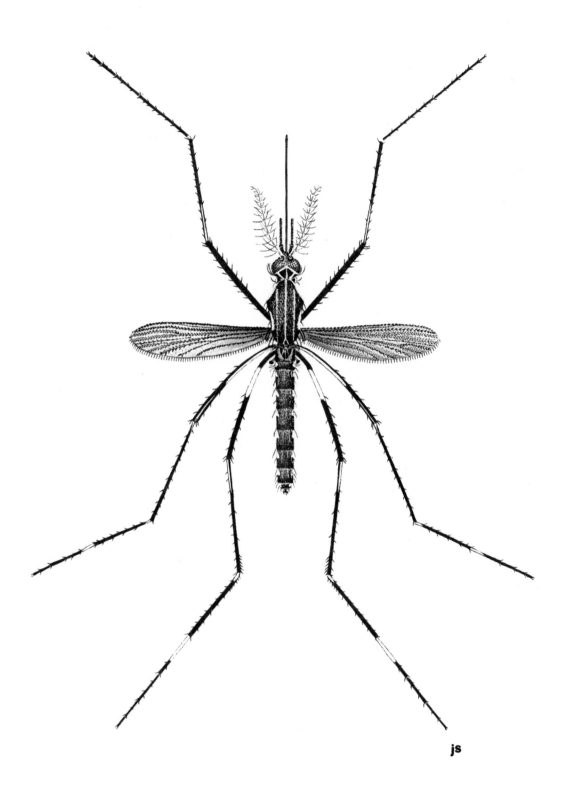

js

Aedes (Stegomyia) aegypti

Small to medium-sized culicine with brilliant silver-white lyre-pattern on thorax and five white rings on hind tarsi.

Head:	Silver white stripe down centre (consisting of two rows of narrowly separated scales).
Proboscis:	Dark.
Palps:	Short — dark at base — outer one-third white.
Thorax:	Silver-white lyre-pattern on dark background (background paler in some specimens, particularly in dry regions or near the coast); two central yellow lines (strings of lyre).
Scutellum:	All white.
Wings:	Dark-scaled except for white dot at base of costa.

Legs:

Front — Femur — white tipped with white line in front.
          Tibia — black.
          Tarsus — segments 1 and 2 with white ring at base; segments 3-5 all black.

Middle — Femur — white tipped with white line in front.
          Tibia — black.
          Tarsus — segments 1 and 2 with white ring at base; segments 3-5 all black.

Hind — Femur — white at tip.
          Tibia — black.
          Tarsus — segments 1-3 with broad white rings at base; segment 4 white except for black tip; segment 5 *usually all white.*

Abdomen:	Pointed; black with white bands at base of segments 2-6; two silver-white spots down each side, conspicuous from above on segment 7.
Distribution:	Throughout the tropics and subtropics.
Feeding Habits:	Variable—one of the most important feeders on man in some regions; not feeding on man in others (mostly dark forms); man-feeding populations feed mostly in the late afternoon, but also to some extent at other times particularly just after dawn. Pale forms feed more often inside houses, dark forms outside.
Resting Habits:	In houses in West Africa; outside houses in East Africa.
Disease Transmission:	Responsible for the transmission of urban yellow fever both in Africa and in the Americas. Outside Africa *A. aegypti* transmits the viruses of the dengue fevers and is presumed to be associated with the spread of haemorrhagic fever. *A. aegypti* has also been associated with the following viruses: chikungunya, Lunyo (variant of Rift Valley fever) and Uganda S. *A. aegypti* also transmits filarial worms.
Breeding Places:	Man-feeding populations of this species usually breed in man-made containers; tins, storage-drums, water-pots, roof-gutters, discarded tyres, bottles, jars, flower pots, and so on; they also breed in broken cocoanut-shells, leaf-axils and almost any small collection of water without earth sides. Non-man feeding populations usually breed in tree-holes.

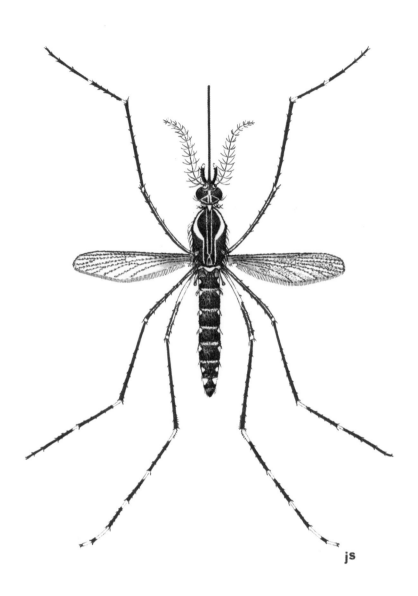

Aedes (Stegomyia) woodi

Small to medium, long and slender culicine, differing from *A. aegypti* (for which it is sometimes mistaken) by black outer lobes to scutellum and all-black fourth hind tarsal segment.

Head: Silver-white stripe down centre.

Proboscis: Dark.

Palps: Short—outer one-third white.

Thorax: Long with silver-white spot on front margin; two silver-white crescent marks and four yellow lines (inner long, outer short).

Scutellum: Middle lobe white; *outer lobes black.*

Wings: Dark-scaled.

Legs: Hind — Tarsus — segments 1 and 2 with narrow white rings at base; segment 3 with wide white ring at base; segment 4 *all black*; segment 5 all white.

Abdomen: Very long and pointed; black with silver-white spots down each side and narrow white bands at base of segments 3-7 (white band on 7 much smaller.)

Distribution: East coast and Malawi.

Feeding Habits: On man in the open.

Resting Habits: On vegetation.

Disease Transmission: Not known.

Breeding Places: In axils of sedge at edges of swamps.

Note: *A. woodi* closely resembles *A. subargenteus* (from Kenya, Tanzania, Malawi, and Zululand) particularly in the markings of the thorax. *A. subargenteus*, however, has the following distinguishing marks: outer lobes of scutellum white; all hind tarsal segments white at base and black at tip.

A. kivuensis (from Rwanda and Tanzania) has segments 4 and 5 of hind tarsi all white.

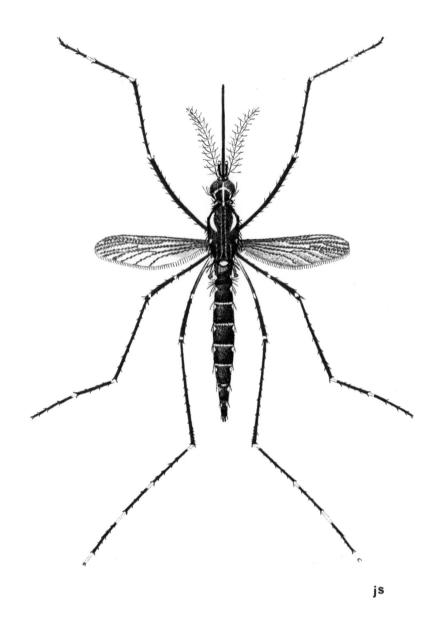

js

Aedes (Stegomyia) simpsoni

Small to medium-sized culicine with two large near-oval silver-white patches on thorax and with fourth hind tarsal segment all black.

Head: Silver-white stripe down centre.

Proboscis: Dark.

Palps: White-tipped.

Thorax: Two large silver-white patches on dark background and four stripes; outer stripes short and white; inner pair longer and yellow except for hind end which is white (the length of the inner stripes varies from almost full length of thorax to being the same length as, or even shorter than, the outer stripes).

Scutellum: All white.

Wings: Dark-scaled.

Legs: Front — Femur — all dark.

           Tibia — narrow white ring at base.

           Tarsus — segments 1 and 2 with narrow white ring at base; segment 3-5 all dark.

    Middle — Femur — black with two white spots on front surface (one beyond middle and one at tip).

           Tibia — all dark.

    Hind — Tarsus — same as front leg.

           Femur — creamy-white near base of front side—turning to white in middle of segment; outer-half black with white spot at tip.

           Tibia — all dark.

           Tarsus — segments 1-3 with white rings at base; *segment 4 all black;* segment 5 all white.

Abdomen: Base of segments 2-6 dull white. Silver-white spots down each side of segments 2-7 and a central silver-white spot on segment 7.

Distribution: Very widespread—from Gambia, Sierra Leone, Ghana and Nigeria in the West to Tanzania, Zanzibar and Malawi in the East and from Sudan and Ethiopia in the North to Transvaal in the South.

Feeding Habits: A. simpsoni occurs in man-feeding and non-man-feeding populations; it feeds outside houses in full sunlight all day long, but with a peak of activity in the mid-afternoon. It is often very common in maize fields.

Resting Habits: Among vegetation.

Disease Transmission: Responsible for the transmission of yellow fever virus from monkey to man and from man to man in rural areas.

Breeding Places: In the leaf axils of pineapples, colocasias (elephant's ears) certain varieties of bananas,* Dracaena and Sansevieria, and in stumps of paw-paw trees. In some regions it is found in tree-holes, and ocasionally in man-made containers.

* In Uganda the bananas include *Gonja* and *Sukali*, but *do not* include *Matoke*.
In Chaggaland, Tanzania, they include *Kibungara*, *Mkonyozi*, *Mkono wa tembo* and *Mzuzu*, but the varieties known as *Kisukari*, *Mchare* and *Mrarao* are of much less importance; *Malindi* is important in some areas.

72

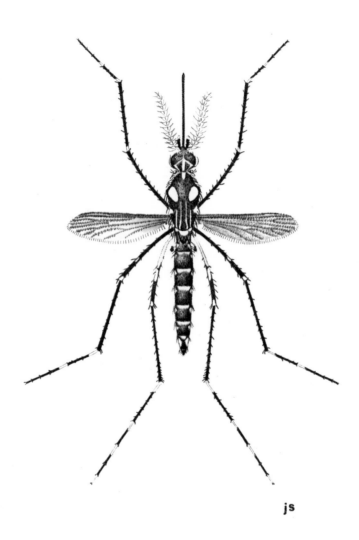

js

Aedes (Stegomyia) metallicus

Small to medium-sized black and white culicine resembling *Aedes simpsoni* but for the presence of three silver-white patches on thorax immediately in front of the scutellum.

Head:	Silver-white stripe down centre.
Proboscis:	Dark.
Palps:	Dark with white tips.
Thorax:	Black with two oval silver-white patches towards front; no yellow lines down centre; *area in front of scutellum largely covered with metallic looking silver-white scales*—usually arranged as two wide elongated patches behind and one smaller patch in front.
Scutellum:	All three lobes covered with silver-white scales.
Wings:	Dark-scaled.

Legs: Black and white.

Front — Femur — black with silver-white patch in front, just before tip.
             Tibia — narrowly white at base.
             Tarsus — segments 1 and 2 with narrow white bases.

Middle — Femur — with two white spots on front surface—one beyond middle, one at tip.
             Tibia — all dark.
             Tarsus — segments 1 and 2 with narrow white bases.

Hind — Femur — with two silver-white patches: one forming a stripe on front surface from base to beyond middle, the other at tip.
             Tibia — all dark.
             Tarsus — segments 1-3 with white rings at base;
                        segment 4 all black;
                        segment 5 white with black tip.

Abdomen:	Black and pointed, with wide white bands at base of tergites 2-6 (band on 6 more silvery than the others); silver-white spots down each side (conspicuous from above on tergite 7).
Distribution:	Widespread and extending both to West and East coasts.
Feeding Habits:	Occasionally on man, outside houses.
Resting Habits:	Probably among vegetation.
Disease Transmission:	Capable of transmitting the virus of yellow fever.
Breeding Places:	Tree holes, banana and other plant axils, cocoanut shells, and sometimes in water-pots and old tins.

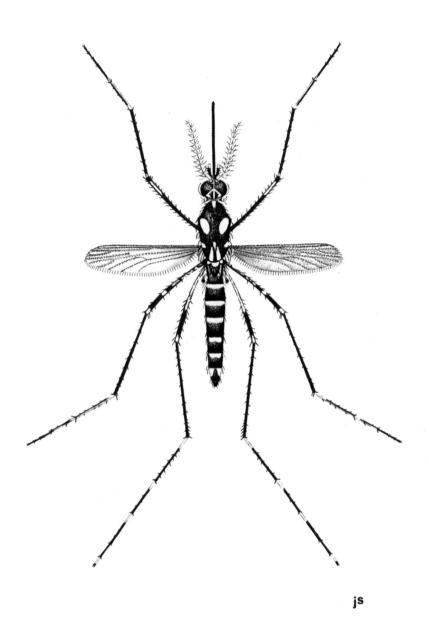

js

Aedes (Stegomyia) apicoargenteus

Small to medium-sized black and white culicine with two round silver-white patches on thorax and black outer lobes to scutellum.

Head: Silver-white stripe down centre.

Proboscis: Dark.

Palps: Dark with white tips.

Thorax: Black with two large round silver-white patches towards front and *three narrow yellow lines* in front of scutellum.

Scutellum: Middle lobe white; *outer lobes black.*

Wings: Dark-scaled.

Legs: Black and white.

Front — Femur — with scattered scales tending to form irregular white line beneath; white spot at tip (additional white spot just beyond middle of middle leg).

Tibia — with small pale patch at base of underside.

Tarsus — segments 1 and 2 with narrow white rings at base.

Middle — Femur — two conspicuous silver-white spots on front surface, one just beyond middle, the other at tip.

Tarsus — segment 1 with narrow white ring at base; segment 2 mainly white above.

Hind — Femur — silver-white stripe on first three-fifths, in front; large silver-white patch at tip.

Tibia — with two white patches, one at base of underside, the other (much larger) on the outer surface extending to about one-third from the base.

Tarsus — segments 1-3 with white rings at base; segment 4 white above except for tip; segment 5 mostly or all black.

Abdomen: Tergites 1-4 usually all black above.
Tergites 5-8 with large silver-white patches in middle.
Tergites 1-7 also with silver-white spots down each side (those on 7 not seen from above).

Distribution: West Africa and eastwards to Uganda, southern Sudan and western Kenya.

Feeding Habits: On man (and probably also on monkeys and perhaps birds) during the mid-day and afternoon period in forested regions. Prefers to feed above ground level in the middle vegetation zone, but will often attack man in large numbers at ground-level.

Resting Habits: Among forest foliage.

Disease
Transmission: Probably not important.

Breeding Places: Mainly in tree-holes, but also in bamboo stumps, water-pots and occasionally in rock-holes.

CLOSELY RELATED SPECIES: *Aedes fraseri* may be readily separated from *A. apicoargenteus* by the following characters:

Thorax Central yellow line extends forwards between the two round white patches and forks just in front of the scutellum. *Lateral lobes of scutellum white.*

Abdomen: Tergites 4-7 with silver-white patches.

Distribution: West Africa and eastwards to Uganda, and western Kenya.

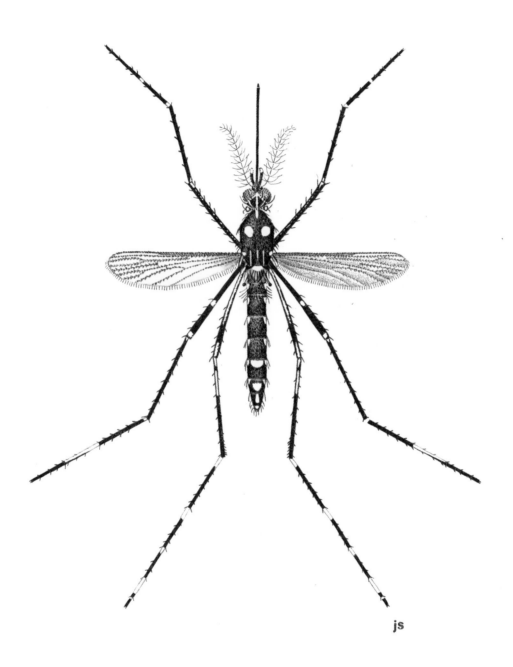

js

Aedes (Stegomyia) de-boeri

Small to medium-sized mainly black and white culicine with a central yellow line running full length of thorax between two large white patches; middle femur without white spot in middle.

Head:	Silver-white stripe down centre.
Proboscis:	Dark.
Palps:	Dark with white tips.
Thorax:	Two large white patches continued back as two narrow yellow lines; long yellow line down centre forking in front of scutellum.
Scutellum:	All three lobes silver-white.
Wings:	Dark-scaled.

Legs:

Front	— Femur	—	all black.
	Tibia	—	black except for white base.
	Tarsus	—	segments 1 and 2 with white ring at base.
Middle	— Femur	—	*without white spot near middle;* white spot near tip.
	Tibia	—	all black.
	Tarsus	—	segments 1 and 2 with white ring at base.
Hind	— Femur	—	white for basal half.
	Tibia	—	creamy-white line at base beneath for one quarter of length.
	Tarsus	—	segment 1-3 with white ring at base; segment 4 nearly all white; segment 5 all black.

Abdomen:	Black and pointed. Tergites 3 (or 4)-7 with pale area at base. Silver-white spots down each side.
Distribution:	Central and East Africa.
Feeding Habits:	On man by day in the open—mostly just before sundown.
Resting Habits:	On forest foliage.
Disease Transmission:	Probably not important.
Breeding Places:	Tree holes.

CLOSELY RELATED SPECIES: *A. dendrophilus, A. demeilloni* and *A. pseudonigeria.*

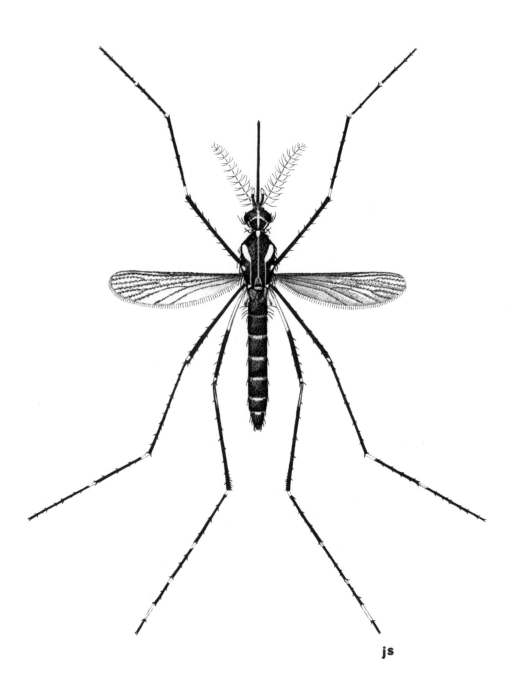

js

Aedes (Stegomyia) africanus

Medium-sized black and white culicine with a pair of narrow crescent-shaped white patches on the thorax, and the third hind tarsal segment all white except for tip.

Head:	Silver-white stripe down centre.
Proboscis:	Dark.
Palps:	Dark with white tips.
Thorax:	Black with two crescent-shaped white patches and three pale yellow lines, one long central line and two short lines towards edges.
Scutellum:	All three lobes white.
Wings:	Dark-scaled.

Legs:

Front — Femur — with silver-white line beneath.
   Tibia — all black.
   Tarsus — segments 1 and 2 (and sometimes 3) white at base.
Middle — Femur — three silver-white patches on front surface.
   Tibia — all black.
   Tarsus — segments 1 and 2 (and sometimes 3) white at base.
Hind — Femur — three silver-white patches on front surface.
   Tibia — large white patch at base beneath.
   Tarsus — segments 1, 2 and 4 with white rings at base;
      segment 3 *all white except for black tip*;
      segment 5 all black.

Abdomen:	Mostly black and pointed. Silver-white spots down each side.
Distribution:	West and Central Africa.
Feeding Habits:	Mainly on monkeys in the forest tree-tops for about half an hour just after sundown. Also feeds on man at ground level during the day.
Resting Habits:	Among foliage.
Disease Transmission:	Responsible for the maintenance of yellow fever in populations of forest monkeys. Occasional transmitter of yellow fever virus from monkey to man. Other viruses — chikungunya, Lunyo, Rift Valley fever and Zika.
Breeding Places:	Mainly tree-holes, rot-holes in buttress roots of trees; occasionally in domestic containers and shaded rock-holes.

CLOSELY RELATED SPECIES: *A. pseudoafricanus*—found in mangrove swamps on the west coast.

 A. ruwenzori—found near the tree-line on the Ruwenzori mountains on the Uganda-Congo border.

 A. luteocephalus—found in comparatively dry regions; it closely resembles *A. africanus* but may be distinguished by its conspicuously yellow-scaled head, by the presence of a yellow line down the centre of the thorax which forks just in front of the scutellum, and by the narrow white ring at the base of the hind femur.

 A. opok (from Acholi, Uganda) differs from *A. luteocephalus* by having the base of the hind femur black; it differs from the others by the much shorter white line at the base of the hind tibia.

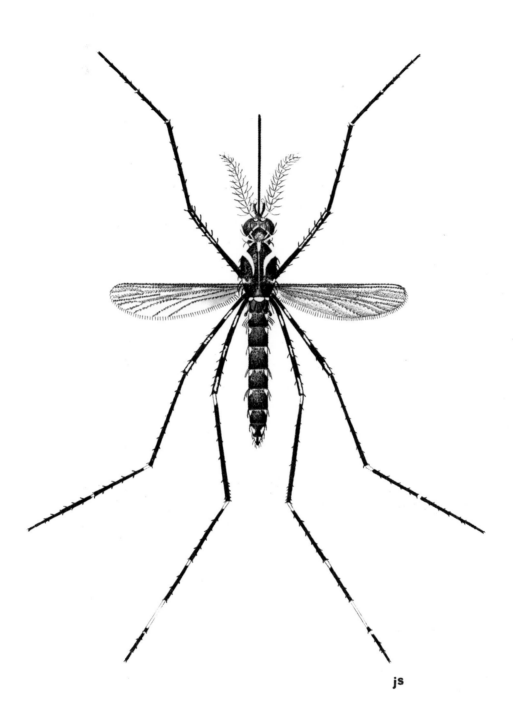

Aedes (Stegomyia) vittatus

Small to medium-sized black (or dark brown) and white culicine with six white spots on the thorax and distinctive leg markings.

Proboscis:	Dark.
Palps:	Mainly dark but with white tips.
Thorax:	Dark with six white spots (arranged in two rows of three).
Scutellum:	Outer lobes white; middle lobe white with a few black scales at tip.
Wings:	Dark-scaled.

Legs: All legs — Femora — scattered white scales on dark background, white tips and a white ring just before tip.

Tibiae — white patch near base and *a white ring near middle*.

Front
and   — Tarsi — segments 1-3 with broad white ring at base.
Middle

Hind   — Tarsus — segments 1-2 first third white;
segment 3 first half white;
segment 4 white except for black tip;
segment 5 all white.

Abdomen:	Dark and pointed, with white bands at base of each tergite.
Distribution:	Very widely spread almost throughout the continent.
Feeding Habits:	Common on man by day in the open, often feeding in full sunlight.
Resting Habits:	Not recorded.
Disease Transmission:	Capable of transmitting the virus of yellow fever.
Breeding Places:	In rock pools, but also occasionally in hoof-prints, water-logged canoes, and sometimes in domestic utensils and in some parts of Africa in tree-holes.

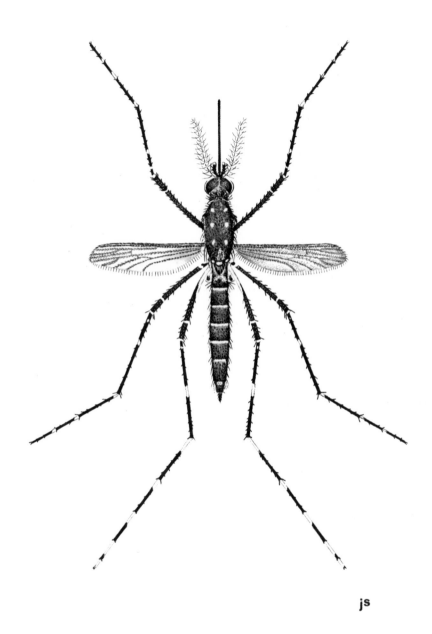

js

83

Aedes (Aedimorphus) haworthi

Medium-sized brown culicine with silver-white base to antennae, white-ringed hind tarsi and a broad silver-white stripe on each "shoulder" of thorax.

Antennae:	Conspicuous white scales on basal segment (torus).
Thorax:	Reddish-brown with a brilliant silver-white stripe along the front half of each side. No white spots in middle of scutum.
Scutellum:	Brilliant silver-white.
Wings:	Dark except for silver-white spot at base of costa.
Legs:	Variable but with all femora white at tip but *without white spot* near tip. All tibiae largely creamy-white beneath; white tips.

Front — Tarsus — *segments 1 and 2 usually white at tip.*
Middle — Tarsus — segment 1 white at tip;
                     segment 2 sometimes white at tip.
Hind — Tibia — white spot at tip twice as long as wide.
         Tarsus — segment 1 white for outer quarter;
                     segments 2-4 white for outer one-third; dark or white at base; segment 5 all white.

Abdomen:	Mainly dark; two small basal silver-white spots at side of each tergite (inconspicuous from above except on tergites 6 and 7).
Distribution:	East coast but extending southwards to Transvaal.
Feeding Habits:	On man outside houses by day.
Resting Habits:	On foliage of plants and trees.
Disease Transmission:	Not important.
Breeding Places:	Mainly in tree-holes, cut bamboos and paw-paw stumps; also found from time to time in borrow-pits and other man-made collections of water.

CLOSELY RELATED SPECIES: with *scutellum* mainly white, and with broad *white bands* on hind tarsal segments.

1 Antenna with basal segment (torus) covered in white scales – – – – – – – – – 2
    Antenna with torus bare or with dark scales only – – – – – – – – – – 7
2 Thorax with four white spots (one on each shoulder and 2 near middle); femora with extra white spot near tip – – – – – – – – – – – – – – – – *A. marshallii.*
    Thorax with white stripe on shoulders; femora *without* extra white spot near tip – – – – – 3
3 Thorax with two white spots in middle – – – – – – – – – – – – – 4
    Thorax without white spots – – – – – – – – – – – – – 5
4 Front and middle tarsi—usually only segment 1 (occasionally 2) with white tip – – – – – *A. capensis.*
    Spots on thorax yellowish, with a yellow line extending back from each towards scutellum; front tarsal segments 1–4 white at tip – – – – – – – – – – – – – *A. kapretwae.*
5 White shoulder-stripe short – – – – – – – – – – – – *A. stokesi.*
    White shoulder-stripe long – – – – – – – – – – – – 6
6 White shoulder-stripe confined to front half – – – – – – – – *A. haworthi, A. ngong.*
    White shoulder-stripe continued to hind margin – – – – – – – – *A. teesdalei.*
7 Thorax with four white spots (one on each shoulder and two near middle) – – – – – *A. simulans.*
    Thorax without white spots – – – – – – – – – – *A. apicoannulatus.*

Note: It is possible that at least *A. capensis*, *A. kapretwae* and *A. stokesi* will one day come to be considered as local forms or subspecies of *A. marshallii* or even merely as variants of a single polymorphic species.

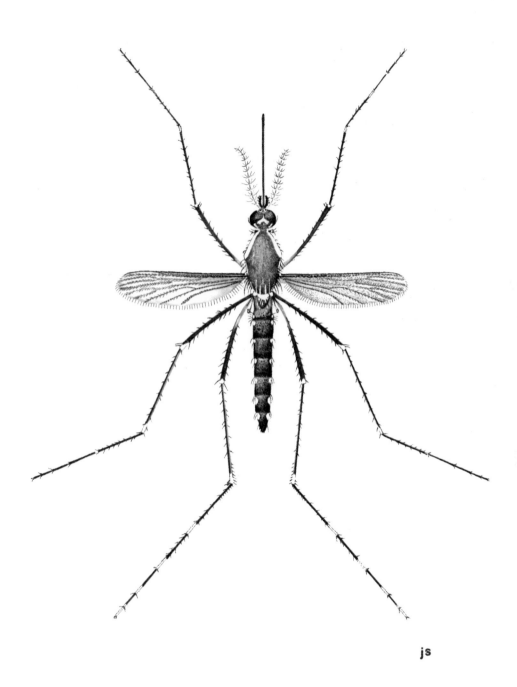

js

Aedes (Aedimorphus) domesticus

Medium-sized brown culicine with a silver-white spot on each shoulder and all-dark tarsi.

Palps: Black or dark brown.

Antennae: No white scales on torus.

Thorax: Reddish-brown with a silver-white spot on each shoulder.

Scutellum: All three lobes covered with silver-white scales.

Wings: Dark-scaled.

Legs: Mainly dark.
All femora with white tip.
All tarsi—black.
Hind — Femur — with additional white spot in front.
Tibia — white area at tip almost one-fifth length of segment.

Abdomen: Mainly dark above—only the silver-white spots on segment 7 can usually be seen from above.

Distribution: Mainly West Africa but extending eastwards as far as Uganda.

Feeding Habits: On man in the open, mainly by day—common in forest.

Resting Habits: On plants.

Disease
Transmission: Not important.

Breeding Places: Open pools.

CLOSELY RELATED SPECIES:

1 Brown culicine with white scutellum and banded hind tarsi – – *A. marshallii* and *A. haworthi* group.
  Brown culicine with white scutellum and black hind tarsi – – – – – – – – – 2
2 Thorax with four white spots – – – – – – – – – – – – 3
  Thorax with two white spots – – – – – – – – – – – – 5
3 Middle and hind femora white-tipped and with *additional white spot* near tip – – – *A. argenteopunctatus.*
  Middle and hind femora *without* additional white spot – – – – – – – – – 4
4 Tori without white scales; palps all dark—*A. punctothoracis* group (including *A. hopkinsi*, *A. mixtus*, *A. microstictus*, *A. mutilus*, and *A. bedfordi*, the females of which cannot be distinguished from *A. punctothoracis*).
  Tori with white scales; palps white-tipped, tibiae with scattered white scales – – *A. insolens* (W. Uganda)
5 Hind tibia with white tip almost one-fifth length of tibia – – – – – – – *A. domesticus*
  A. longiseta
  A. ovazzai

  Hind tibia with white tip only about one-eighth length of tibia – – – – – *A. leptolabis.*

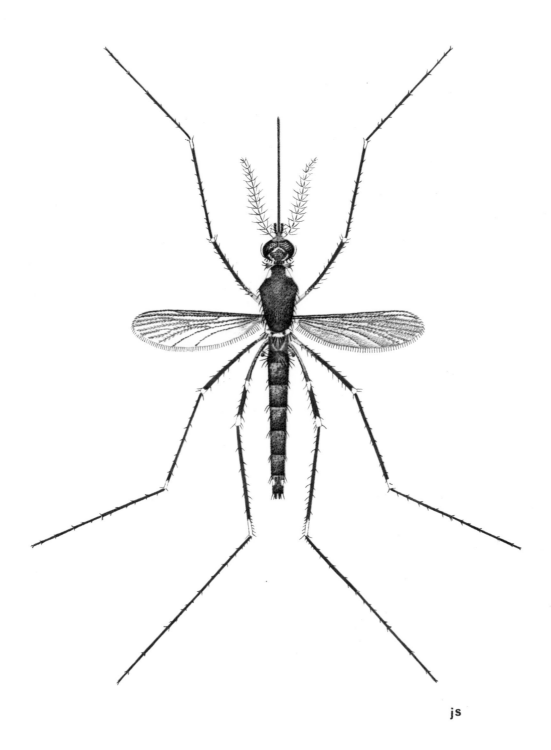

js

87

Aedes (Aedimorphus) cumminsii

Large brown culicine with pointed abdomen but without any really distinctive markings; scales on back of head all pale.

Palps:	Brown.
Thorax:	Brown.
Scutellum:	Brown.
Wings:	Dark-scaled; upper forked vein distinctly longer than lower.
Legs:	Dark with pale spot at tip of femora. Hind — Femur — pale in front almost to tip. Tibia — pale spot at tip. Tarsus — dark; claws toothed.
Abdomen:	Usually all dark above; underside with narrow black bands along hind edge of each segment.
Distribution:	Sudan, East and West Africa and eastern Congo.
Feeding Habits:	On man mainly outside houses both by day and by night.
Resting Habits:	Mainly on forest foliage but occasionally in houses.
Disease Transmission:	Spondweni virus.
Breeding Places:	Muddy-water in temporary pools.

CLOSELY RELATED SPECIES: *A. holocinctus* (East Africa) has wide pale bands on the abdomen above.

    A. quasiunivittatus (East Africa: from Sudan and Ethiopia in north to Transvaal in south) has banded abdomen, *simple* hind claws and a patch of dark scales in the middle of the head above.

    A. dentatus, similar in distribution and abdominal markings to *A. quasinunivittatus*, but with hind claws toothed.

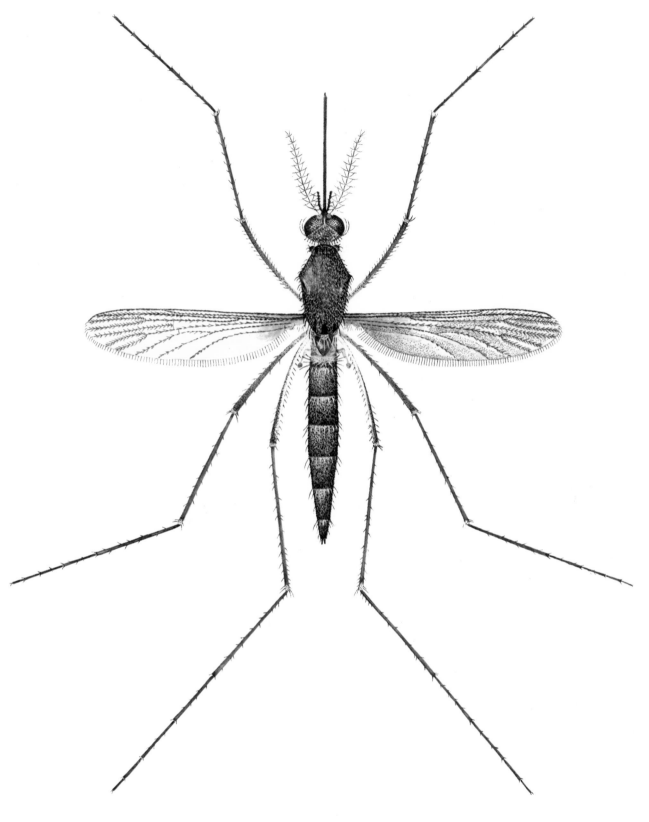

js

Aedes (Neomelaniconion) circumluteolus

Medium-sized brown culicine with yellow borders to thorax and banded abdomen.

Head: Yellow scales on top (sometimes very pale).

Proboscis: Very dark; slightly longer than front femora.

Palps: Dark.

Antennae: Basal segment (torus) usually yellow except for inner side (all dark in some specimens).

Thorax: Yellow bands down each side of scutum meeting in front; two patches of yellow scales in front of scutellum sometimes continued forward as two faint yellow lines.

Scutellum: Dark with yellow scales.

Wings: Vein 5 with mainly yellow scales.

Legs: Mainly rather dark.
Middle — Tibia — pale above towards tip.
Hind — Femur — first half yellowish in front.
Tibia — pale beneath except for tip.

Abdomen: Central patch of yellow scales on tergite 1.
Basal pale band on tergites 2-7; *mainly pale yellow scales on underside.*

Distribution: Very widely distributed.

Feeding Habits: On man by day and by night but mostly just before sun-down; feeds mostly outside houses both in open country and in forest.

Resting Habits: Among grass and other low-growing plants; also in houses.

Disease Transmission: More viruses have so far been isolated from *A. circumluteolus* than from any other African species:
Bunyamwera, Kamese, Middleburg, Ndumu, Pongola, Rift Valley fever, Simbu, Spondweni, and Wesselsbron.

Breeding Places: Mainly associated with grass and other vegetation in ground-pools and at the edge of swamps, following periods of heavy rain. Sometimes also found in animal foot-prints.

CLOSELY RELATED SPECIES: *A. lineatopennis* (very widely distributed, extending to India and the Philippines) may be distinguished by the abdomen having mainly dark scales on underside.

A. taeniorostris group have complete or incomplete yellow ring on proboscis and unbanded abdomen.

A. palpalis has all dark proboscis but unbanded abdomen.

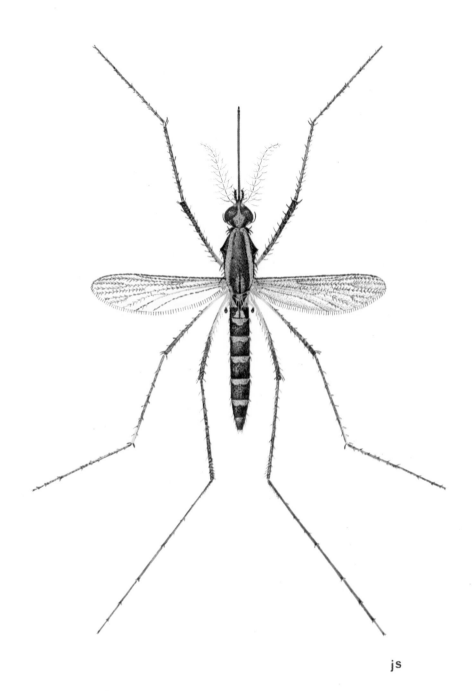

js

Aedes (Diceromyia) taylori

Small, heavily-scaled culicine with white-ringed tarsi.

Proboscis:	Dark with pale ring near middle.
Palps:	Dark with two white rings (one near base the other near middle).
Thorax:	Hairy with a mixture of brown and yellowish scales.
Scutellum:	Covered mostly with white scales, but some dark scales usually present.
Wings:	Covered with large brown and large white scales (resembling those of *Mansonia*).
Legs:	All legs — Femora and Tibiae — with a mixture of black and white scales.
	Tarsi — each segment black with a white ring at base; some scattered white scales on segment 1.
Abdomen:	Mainly dark, narrow wedge-shaped pale bands on each tergite and scattered yellow scales.
	Segment 8 with white line down centre.
Distribution:	Sudan, West, East and southern Africa.
Feeding Habits:	Mostly in the forest canopy.
Resting Habits:	Not recorded.
Disease Transmission:	Capable of transmitting yellow fever virus; chikungunya virus has also been isolated from this species.
Breeding Places:	Tree holes.

CLOSELY RELATED FORMS: *A. furcifur* (distribution the same). Females impossible to distinguish from *A. taylori*; also capable of transmitting yellow fever virus.

A. adersi (East Coast): no complete pale ring on proboscis although there may be some scattered pale scales near middle; femora with white base in front.

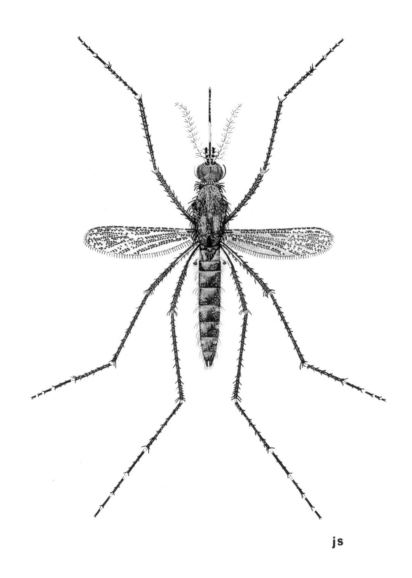

js

93

Culex tigripes

Large culicine with dark proboscis and pale-spotted legs.

Proboscis:	Dark, but usually with some pale scales near middle of underside.
Palps:	Dark with a few pale scales near middle of innerside.
Thorax:	Mainly dark brown with variable pale markings. Often with pale border and two pale spots near middle, and sometimes a third near front.
Wings:	Dark-scaled.

Legs:

Front and Middle — Femora and tibiae dark with a row of about ten pale spots on front surface.
Tarsi — dark.

Hind — Femur — irregular mottling on outer surface.
Tibia — with a row of pale spots on outer surface, which run together on the inner surface.
Tarsus — dark (segment 1 occasionally pale beneath).

Abdomen:	Very variable in colour; blunt tip. Tergites may be almost entirely dark or may have yellowish bands on margins. Tergites 6-8 entirely yellow in some specimens.
Distribution:	Very widely distributed throughout the continent, including the islands of Fernando Po, Madagascar and Mauritius.
Feeding Habits:	At times *C. tigripes* attacks man, mainly outside houses by day.
Resting Habits:	Vegetation.
Disease Transmission:	Not important.
Breeding Places:	Very widely distributed in many different types of water: swamps, tree-holes. leaf-axils of plants and artificial containers of every sort. The larvae feed on other mosquito larvae (both anopheline and culicine).

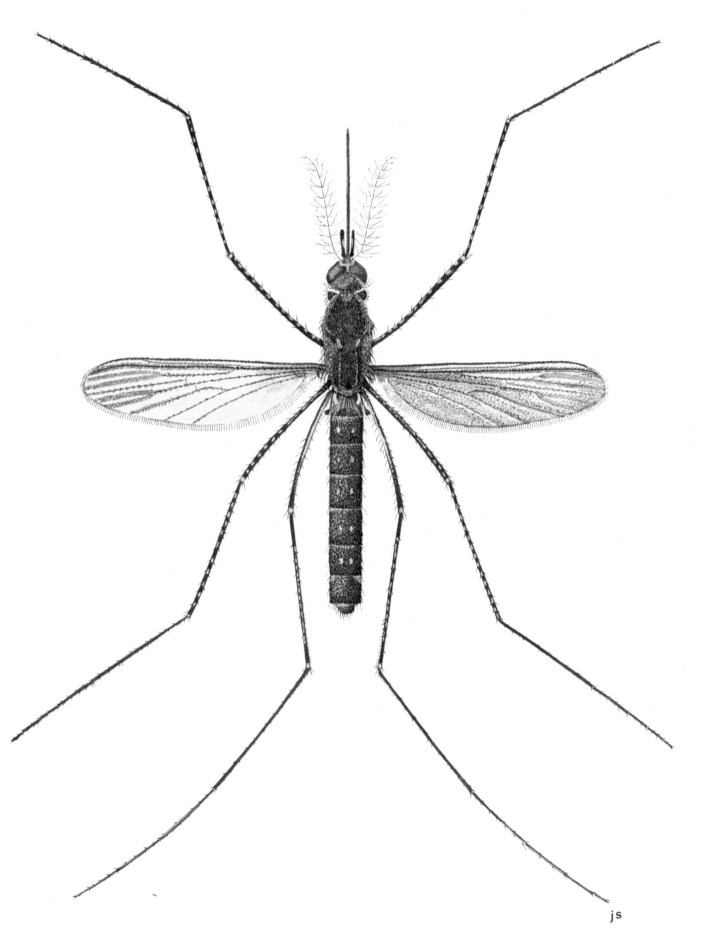

js

Culex poicilipes

Medium to large culicine resembling *C. tigripes* with its pale-spotted legs, but distinguished by the pale ring near the middle of the proboscis.

Proboscis:	Dark with a clearly-defined, pale yellowish ring near middle.
Palps:	Dark with a few pale scales at tip, and just below middle.
Thorax:	Varies from light-brown to black, often with a band of pale (yellow or white) scales behind the middle. In light specimens the pale area may cover front two-thirds of the scutum. In darker specimens the pale area is reduced to two pale spots.
Wings:	Dark-scaled.
Legs:	All legs — Femora and Tibiae — dark with a row of seven to ten yellow spots. Tarsi — pale rings at joints of segments (very small on joint 4-5 of hind tarsus).
Abdomen:	Variable in colour; blunt tip. In light specimens, tergites 1-7 may have yellowish or white bands along front margin. In dark specimens, tergite 2 with single yellowish spot.
Distribution:	Very common throughout Africa, ranging from Egypt and Ethiopia in the north to Zululand in the south, and from Ghana in the west to the islands of Madagascar and Mauritius off the east coast.
Feeding Habits:	Occasionally on man, mainly outside houses by day.
Resting Habits:	Various.
Disease Transmission:	Not important.
Breeding Places:	Ditches, pools in swamps, and pools in river beds. Usually associated with clear water and vegetation.

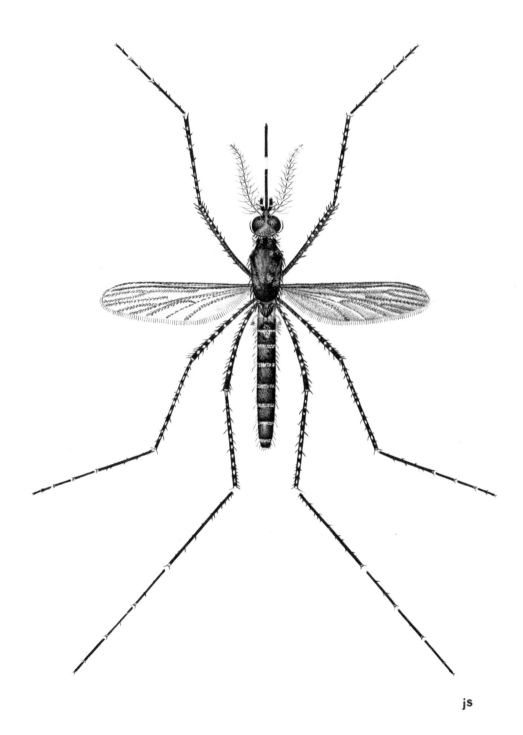

js

Culex annulioris

Medium to large culicine with ringed proboscis and pale scales on front two-thirds of thorax (resembling *C. poicilipes*, but *without pale spots on legs*).

Proboscis:	Dark with a clearly defined pale ring near middle.
Palps:	Dark with some white scales at tip.
Thorax:	Mottled-brown. In many specimens there is a band of pale scales behind middle, the pale scales sometimes occupying the front two thirds.
Wings:	Mainly dark-scaled but a few pale scales, mainly on costa, subcosta and on veins 1 and 5.
Legs:	All legs — Femora and tibiae with a sprinkling of pale scales (not forming distinct spots). Tarsi — pale rings at joints.
Abdomen:	Blunt-tipped. Typically with pale scales on dark background. Segments 2-7 with pale patch at middle of base of each tergite; and a pair of pale triangles at hind edges. Mainly dark beneath. Subspecies *C. a. consimilis* (West Africa)—tergites black.
Distribution:	Very widespread.
Feeding Habits:	On man occasionally, by day and by night.
Resting Habits:	In side and outside houses.
Disease Transmission:	Ntaya and Kamese viruses have been recovered from this species.
Breeding Places:	In clear water containing filamentous algae.

CLOSELY RELATED SPECIES: *Culex bitaeniorhynchus* group: large species also possessing pale ring on proboscis, ringed tarsi and tendency towards pale scaling on front two-thirds of thorax; proboscis sometimes with pale tip.

C. *bitaeniorhynchus* (widespread in Africa and Asia): Proboscis with pale tip; pale scales on thorax usually reduced to two yellowish spots behind middle; abdomen without pale triangles but with yellow spots at outer edges of tergites 5-8; tergites 6-8 sometimes entirely yellow.

C. *ethiopicus* (widespread): female very similar indeed to C. *bitaeniorhynchus* but usually paler and with a clearly defined pale area on front two-thirds of thorax and broad yellowish bands on tergites 2-7.

C. *aurantapex* (East Africa): Resembling the darker forms of C. *bitaeniorhynchus* but with wings almost entirely dark-scaled; tip of proboscis black (as in C. *annulioris*); thorax dark with a few scattered pale scales; abdomen black except for orange-coloured tergites 5-8.

C. *giganteus* (Madagascar): Larger but otherwise similar to typical C. *annulioris* (perhaps it ought really to be regarded as a local subspecies—C. *annulioris giganteus*).

C. *sitiens* group resembles C. *bitaeniorhynhcus* and C. *annulioris* in having ringed proboscis and ringed tarsi, but are much smaller and do not have pale scales on front part of scutum.

C. *sitiens* (Red Sea area and East Coast) has speckled femora.

C. *thalassius* (widespread) darker and without speckling on femora.

C. *tritaeniorhynchus* (West Africa, also Kenya, Mozambique, Mauritius, Zanzibar and eastwards into Asia as far as Japan). Pale scales at base of proboscis in addition to pale ring in middle; tarsal rings narrow and indistinct.

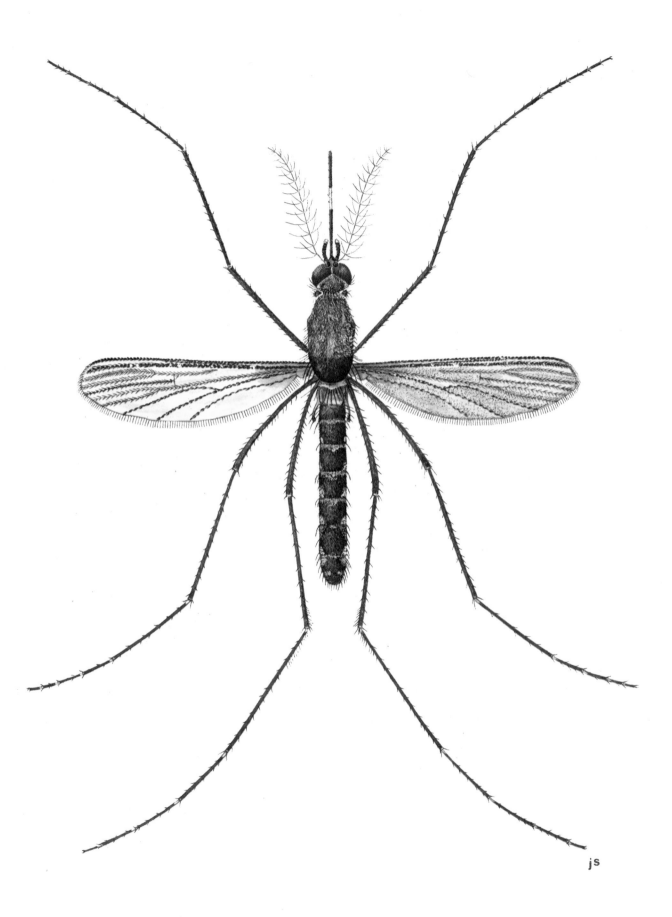

js

99

Culex argenteopunctatus

Small dark culicine with four silver-white spots on thorax (resembling *Aedes*) but with typical blunt-tipped abdomen of *Culex*.

Proboscis:	Black above, pale in middle beneath.
Palps:	Black.
Thorax:	Dark with four silver-white spots—two on front edge and two larger ones in middle.
Scutellum:	All three lobes with silver-white scales.
Wings:	Dark-scaled.
Legs:	Mainly dark. Middle — Femur — *silver-white spot at tip.* Hind — Femur — white at base; front surface white for four-fifths length; last one-fifth black with white spot at tip. Tibia — silver-white spot at tip.
Abdomen:	Dark (white spots near sides do not show from above) and blunt-tipped.
Distribution:	Fairly widespread from Ghana in the west to Malawi in the east and from Sudan in the north to Rhodesia, Natal and South West Africa.
Feeding Habits:	On man outside houses mainly by day.
Resting Habits:	On vegetation.
Disease Transmission:	Not important:
Breeding Places:	Ground pools (larva with very long siphon).

Note: The description above applies to *C. argenteopunctatus kingi; C. a. argenteopunctatus* (from Madagascar only) lacks the white base to the hind femur.

Care must be taken to distinguish *C. argenteopunctatus* from *Aedes (Aedimorphus) argenteopunctatus*, which also has four silver-white spots similarly placed on the thorax and all three lobes of scutellum silver-white.

Aedes argenteopunctatus has the following characteristics which distinguish it from *C. argenteopunctatus*.

Abdomen	— pointed.
Wings:	— with silver-white spot at base of costa.
Legs:	— Front—Femur and tibia with white tip.
Middle and Hind	Femora with white spot on front surface just before tip (in addition to white tip).

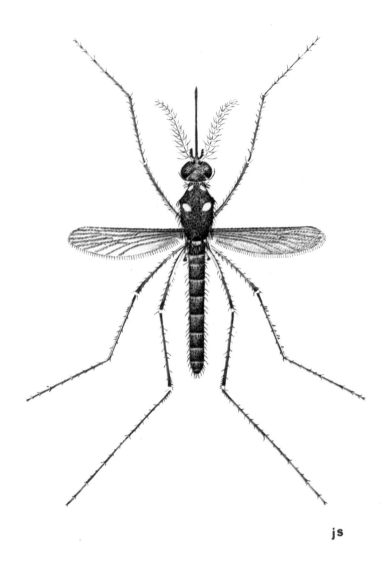

js

Culex pipiens fatigans

Medium-sized culicine with brown thorax and striped abdomen.

Proboscis:	Dark above, mainly pale beneath.
Palps:	Dark.
Antennae:	First segment largely pale.
Thorax:	Scutum uniformly brown, reddish-brown or pale brown.
Wings:	Dark-scaled.
Legs:	Mainly dark. Hind — Tibia — with pale, often inconspicuous, spot at tip.
Abdomen:	Distinctly rounded or blunt at tip; dark above with white or creamy bands along base of each tergite (widening towards centre of tergite); largely pale scales beneath.
Distribution:	It is the commonest nuisance-mosquito in most urban and semi-urban parts of Africa from Khartoum to Cape Town (and indeed throughout much of the tropical and subtropical world).
Feeding Habits:	In some places *C. p. fatigans* feeds on man in very great numbers, both inside and outside houses by night. In other places *C. p. fatigans*, or other subspecies of *C. pipiens*, feed mainly on birds.
Resting Habits:	Very common in houses.
Disease Transmission:	*C. p. fatigans* is the main transmitter of the filarial worm, *Wuchereria bancrofti*, heavy infections of which may lead to elephantiasis. West Nile and chikungunya viruses have also been recovered from *C. p. fatigans*.
Breeding Places:	In drains, gulley-traps, pit latrines, motor-tyres, domestic water-containers, old cocoanut shells and so on. It will breed in the foulest water.

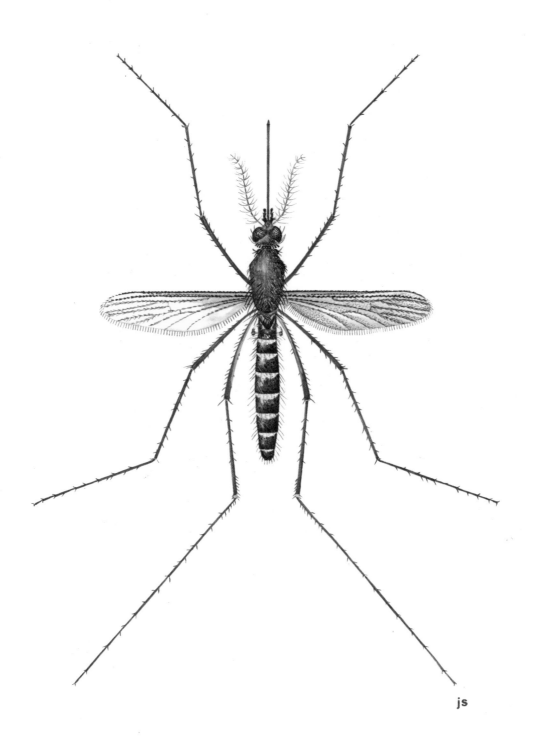

js

REFERENCES

EVANS, A. M. (1938) *Mosquitoes of the Ethiopian Region. II—Anophelini, Adults and Early Stages.* British Museum (Nat. Hist.): London.

EDWARDS, F. W. (1941) *Mosquitoes of the Ethiopian Region. III—Culicine Adults and Pupae.* British Museum (Nat. Hist.): London.

GILLETT, J. D. (1971) *Mosquitos.* Weidenfeld and Nicolson, London.

HOPKINS, G. H. E. (1951) *Mosquitoes of the Ethiopian Region. I—Larval Bionomics of Mosquitoes and Taxonomy of Culicine Larvae.* British Museum (Nat. Hist.): London.

HADDOW, A. J., van SOMEREN, E. C. C., LUMSDEN, W. H. R., HARPER, J. O., and GILLETT, J. D. (1951) The mosquitoes of Bwamba County, Uganda, VIII. Records of occurrence and habitat. *Bull. ent. Res. 42:* 207-238.

GILLIES, M. T. and de MEILLON, B. (1968) *The Anophelinae of Africa South of the Sahara (Ethiopian Zoogeographical Region).* S. African Inst. Med. Res. Johannesburg.

MAYR, E. (1942). *Systematics and the Origin of Species.* Columbia Univ. Press, N.Y.

STONE, A., KNIGHT, K. L. and STARCKE, H. (1959) *A Synoptic Catalog of the Mosquitoes of the World (Diptera, Culicidae).* Thomas Say Foundation, 6, Ent. Soc. Amer. (and supplements I-IV).

INDEX TO VIRUSES

	PAGE
Bunyamwera	7, 50, 90
Bwamba fever	18, 48, 50
Chikungunya	42, 48, 50, 68, 80, 92, 102
Kamese	90, 98
Lunyo	68, 80
Middleburg	90
Ndumu	48, 90
Nkolbisson	56
Ntaya	98
Nyando	18
Okola	56
O'nyong-nyong	18, 26
Pongola	50, 90
Rift Valley fever	42, 48, 50, 56, 68, 80, 90
Simbu	90
Sindbis	30, 42, 50
Spondweni	48, 50, 88, 90
Tanga	18
Uganda S	62, 64, 68
Usutu	44
Wesselsbron	48, 90
West Nile	36, 102
Yellow fever	50, 56, 62, 68, 72, 74, 80, 82
Zika	80

INDEX TO SPECIES

Species described in full and illustrated are printed in bold

		PAGE			PAGE
Aedeomyia	africana	54	Aedes	**pulchrithorax**	66, 67
	furfurea	54, 55		punctothoracis	86
Aedes	adersi	92		quasiunivittatus	88
	aegypti	3, 4, 68, 69, 70		ruwenzori	80
	africanus	80, 81		**simpsoni**	2, 3, 72, 73, 74
	apicoannulatus	84		simulans	84
	apicoargenteus	76, 77		stokesi	84
	argenteopunctatus	86, 100		subargenteus	70
	barnardi	66		taeniorostris	90
	bedfordi	86		**taylori**	92, 93
	capensis	84		teesdalei	84
	circumluteolus	90, 91		**vittatus**	82, 83
	cumminsii	88, 89		wellmani	64
	de-boeri	78, 79		**woodi**	70, 71
	demeilloni	78	Anopheles	aruni	18
	dendrophilus	78		brucei	18
	dentatus	88		caliginosus	7, 8
	domesticus	86, 87		**christyi**	24, 25
	embuensis	64		confusus	18
	fraseri	76		**coustani**	3, 7, 8, 9
	fulgens	62		cydippus	32
	furcifur	92		dthali	14
	hancocki	66		**funestus**	4, 18, 19
	haworthi	84, 85, 86		fuscivenosus	18
	holocinctus	88		**gambiae**	26, 27
	hopkinsi	86		**garnhami**	22, 23
	ingrami	64, 65		gibbinsi	16
	insolens	86		hargreavesi	16
	kapretwae	84		**implexus**	10, 11
	kivuensis	70		leesoni	18
	leptolabis	86		**maculipalpis**	28
	lineatopennis	90		marshallii	16
	longipalpis	62, 63, 64		melas	26
	longiseta	86		merus	26
	luteocephalus	80		**moucheti**	16, 17
	marshallii	84, 86		**nili**	12, 13
	metallicus	74, 75		paludis	7, 8
	microstictus	86		parensis	18
	mixtus	86		**pharoensis**	30, 31
	mutilus	86		**rhodesiensis**	14, 15
	mzooi	62		rivulorum	18
	ngong	84		somalicus	12
	nyasae	64		**squamosus**	32, 33
	opok	80		swahilicus	32
	ovazzai	86		symesi	7, 8
	palpalis	90		tenebrosus	7, 8
	pembaensis	7		**wellcomei**	20, 21
	pseudoafricanus	80		ziemanni	7, 8
	pseudonigeria	78	Coquillettidia	annettii	40

		PAGE
Coquillettidia	aurea	44
	aurites	44, 45, 46
	fraseri. . . .	46, 47
	fuscopennata . . .	42, 43
	maculipennis . .	40, 41
	metallica . . .	5, 36, 37
	microannulata	44
	pseudoconopas . .	38, 39
Culex	**annulioris** . . .	98, 99
	argenteopunctatus . .	100, 101
	aurantapex	98
	bitaeniorhynchus . . .	98
	ethiopicus	98
	giganteus	98
	pipiens . . .	102, 103
	poicilipes . . .	96, 97, 98
	pulchrithorax . . .	66
	sitiens	98
	thalassius	98
	tigripes . .	7, 94, 95, 96
	tritaeniorhynchus . . .	98
Culiseta	fraseri	7
	longiareolata . . .	7
Eretmapodites	argyrus	58
	chrysogaster . .	4, 56, 57
	corbeti. . . .	60

		PAGE
Eretmapodites	dracaenae	60
	forcipulatus	58
	gilletti	56
	grahami	56
	haddowi	56
	harperi	56
	hightoni	60
	inornatus . . .	58, 59
	intermedius . . .	56
	mahaffyi	56
	mattinglyi	56
	melanopus	58
	pauliani	56
	penicillatus . . .	58
	quinquevittatus . .	60, 61
	semisimplicipes . . .	56
	subsimplicipes . . .	56
	tonsus	60
	vansomerenae . . .	56
Ficalbia	**flavopicta** . . .	34, 35
Hodgesia	cyptopus	52
	nigeriae	52
	psectropus	52
	sanguinae . . .	52, 53
Mansonia	**africana** . .	4, 48, 50, 51
	uniformis . . .	4, 48, 49